Table of Contents

Month 1...3
- the alphabet
- looking at the shapes of letters
- identifying alphabet letters by name
- printing capital and lowercase letters
- matching each letter to its partner
- practicing ABC order
- playing games

Month 2...33
- learning the sounds of *b, c, f, h, m, n, p, r, t,* and *y*
- identifying the sound of short *a* as in *cat*
- working with words in the *-at* and *-an* families
- writing words
- reading stories
- playing games

Month 3..65
- reviewing the letters and sounds from Month 2
- learning the sounds of *g, j, k, l,* and *w*
- identifying the sound of short *e* as in *hen*
- working with words in the *-et* and *-en* families
- writing words
- reading stories
- playing games

Month 4...97
- reviewing the letters and sounds from Month 3
- learning the sounds of *d, q, s, y,* and *z*
- identifying the sound of short *i* as in *pig*
- working with words in the *-in* and *-ig* families
- writing words
- reading stories
- playing games

Month 5...129
- reviewing the letters and sounds from Month 4
- listening for the ending sounds of *b, d, g, m, n, p, t,* and *x*
- learning blends with *-l*
- identifying the sound of short *o* as in *hop*
- working with words in the *-og* and *-op* families
- writing words
- reading stories
- playing games

Month 6...161
- reviewing the letters and sounds from Month 5
- listening for the ending sounds of *k, r, s, ll,* and *ss*
- learning blends with *-r*
- listening for the ending blends and digraphs *ck, nd, ng,* and *nt*
- identifying the sound of short *u* as in *hug*
- working with words in the *-ub* and *-ug* families
- writing words
- reading stories
- playing games

Month 7.................................193
- reviewing the letters and sounds from Month 6
- learning blends with s-
- learning the digraphs *ch, sh, th, wh*
- reviewing the sound of short *a* as in *snap*
- working with words in the *-am* and *-ap* families
- writing words
- reading stories
- playing games

Month 8.................................225
- reviewing the letters and sounds from Month 7
- learning the sounds of soft *c* and soft *g*
- learning to make plurals
- identifying and using the silent *e*
- identifying the sound of long *a* as in *lake*
- working with words with *a_e, ai,* and *ay*
- writing words
- reading stories
- playing games

Month 9.................................257
- reviewing the letters, sounds, and words from Month 8
- learning to make compound words
- learning the meaning of *un-* and *re-*
- learning the meaning of *-ed* and *-ing*
- identifying the sound of long *e* as in *these*
- working with words with *ee* and *ea*
- writing words
- reading stories
- playing games

Month 10.................................289
- reviewing the letters, sounds, and words from Month 9
- identifying the sound of long *i* as in *ride*
- learning the vowel sounds of *y*
- working with words with *i_e, ie, igh,* and *y*
- learning to make contractions with *not, are,* and *will*
- writing words
- reading stories
- playing games

Month 11.................................321
- reviewing the letters, sounds, and words from Month 10
- learning to work with two-syllable words
- identifying the sound of long *o* as in *code*
- working with words with *o_e, oa,* and *oe*
- learning the sounds of *ou* and *ow*; *oi* and *oy*
- learning about homophones, such as *tail* and *tale*
- writing words
- reading stories
- playing games

Month 12.................................353
- reviewing the letters, sounds, and words from Month 11
- identifying the sound of long *u* as in *mule*
- working with words with *u_e, ue,* and *ui*
- identifying the sounds of *oo*
- writing words
- reading stories
- playing games

Index.................................383

Month 1 Checklist

Hands-on activities to help your child in school!

THE ALPHABET

Recognizing and Writing Letters A-Z: pages 5-32

Recognizing and writing the letters of the alphabet is an important first step on the road to learning success. The activities in this section will give your child practice examining the shapes of letters *Aa* to *Zz* while learning to print both capital and small letter forms. Matching capital to small letters and placing letters in *ABC* order are the other essential skills presented to ensure your child's reading and writing progress. In addition to helping your child complete the worksheets for this month, try the following:

❏ Write the letters of the alphabet on index cards, one letter per card. Make one set for capital letters and one set for small letters. Use the cards with your child in the following ways:

- Mix up the stacks and have your child sort them into capital and small letters.
- Place sets of matching capital and small letters facedown on a table in four rows of four cards each. With your child, take turns turning over two cards at a time to find the matching letters. When your child is comfortable with the game, increase the number of cards.
- Take a letter walk with your child. Place one set of cards in order from *A to Z* along a path inside your home or outdoors. As you walk along the path with your child, take turns choosing a card and naming it.
- Have your child hold up a card for you to name. Every now and then, say an incorrect letter name and invite your child to say "gotcha" and name the correct letter. Then reverse roles.
- Give your child a card and have him or her hunt for the letter wherever you go, saying, *"I spy with my little eye* [letter name]*!"*

❏ Randomly name letters and ask your child to print them with a variety of writing tools, such as markers, colored pencils, pens, crayons, and chalk.

❏ Sing *"The Alphabet Song"* together, adding a new verse at the end:

> *Knowing letters A to Z*
> *Is lots of fun for you and me!*

Have your child use kitchen utensils, such as spoons, pans, or plastic cups, to tap the beat as you sing.

❑ Let your child use craft and recycled materials to create a nametag, highlighting the capital letter at the beginning. Explain that the names of people begin with capital letters. Then invite him or her to cut out a picture of a pet from a newspaper or magazine and give the pet a name. Help your child make a nametag for the pet, pointing out that the names of pets also begin with capital letters.

❑ Spread a thin layer of powdered drink or gelatin mix in a pie tin. Have your child print the letter you name in the powder, using his or her finger. Carefully shake the tin to smooth the mix before naming another letter.

❑ Take turns choosing a letter and thinking of a way to work together to form the letter with your arms, hands, fingers, legs, or whole bodies.

❑ Check out several colorful alphabet books from the library. Read the books together, encouraging your child to find or name specific letters.

The Alphabet Song

Sing "The Alphabet Song."

Aa Bb Cc Dd Ee Ff Gg

Hh Ii Jj Kk

Ll Mm Nn Oo Pp

Qq Rr Ss

Tt Uu Vv

Ww Xx

Yy and Zz

Now I
know my ABCs.
Next time won't you sing
with me?

Reciting the letters of the alphabet

ALPHABET

5

The Letter Aa

 Trace the hollow letters with your finger. Then trace the other letters with a pencil. Now write the letters.

 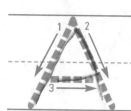  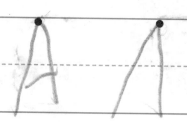

   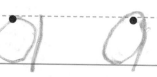

Circle each ant that has **A** or **a** on it.

Recognizing and writing **Aa**

The Letter Bb

 Trace the hollow letters with your finger. Then trace the other letters with a pencil. Now write the letters.

 **Bb**

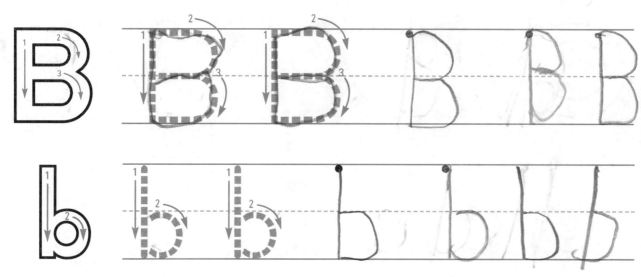

 B and **b** go together. They are partner letters. Color each balloon that has partner letters.

The Letter Cc

Trace the hollow letters with your finger. Then trace the other letters with a pencil. Now write the letters.

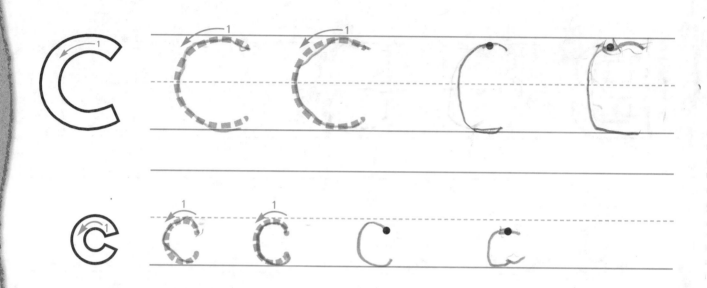

C and c go together. They are partner letters. Circle each car that has partner letters.

Recognizing and writing Cc

The Letter Dd

 Trace the hollow letters with your finger. Then trace the other letters with a pencil. Now write the letters.

Dd

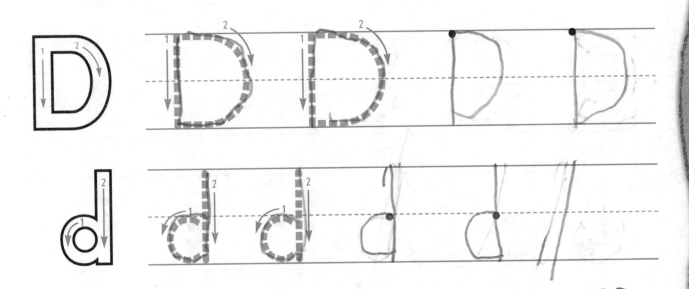

Find and circle each **D** and **d** in the picture.

Recognizing and writing Dd

The Letter Ee

 Trace the hollow letters with your finger. Then trace the other letters with a pencil. Now write the letters.

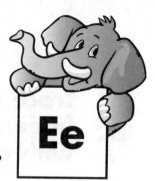

Ee

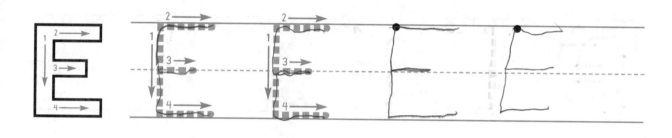

 E and **e** go together. They are partner letters. Draw a line from the letter on each elephant to its partner letter.

*Recognizing and writing **Ee***

The Letter Ff

Trace the hollow letters with your finger. Then trace the other letters with a pencil. Now write the letters.

Ff

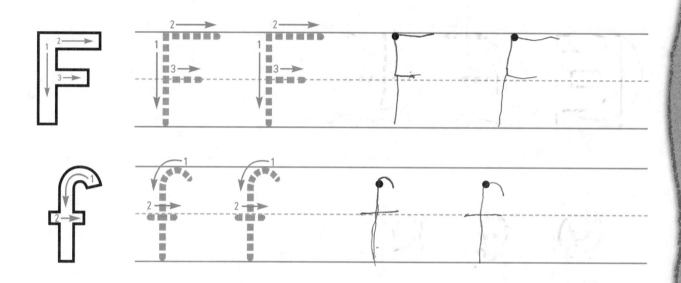

Draw a line through three letters **F** or **f** on each game. Then you will win tic-tac-toe!

The Letter Gg

Trace the hollow letters with your finger. Then trace the other letters with a pencil. Now write the letters.

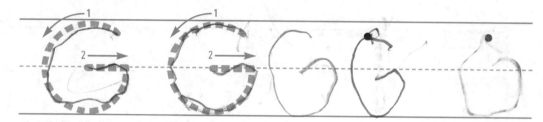

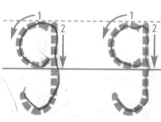
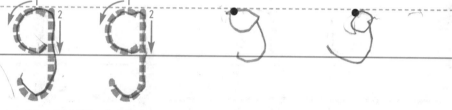

Color the letters **G** and **g**.
What will the gorilla play?

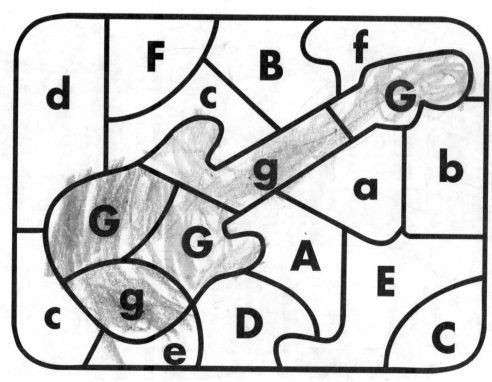

The Letter Hh

 Trace the hollow letters with your finger. Then trace the other letters with a pencil. Now write the letters.

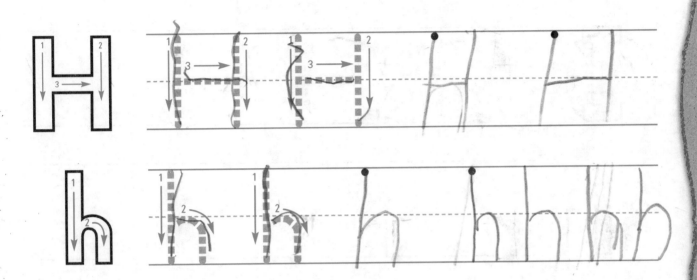

 Help Howard Hippo get to Howie, his son. Follow the letters **H** and **h** to draw a path through the maze.

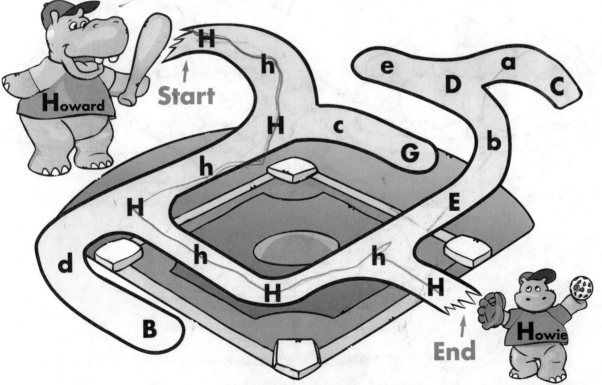

Recognizing and writing **Hh**

The Letter Ii

 Trace the hollow letters with your finger. Then trace the other letters with a pencil. Now write the letters.

 Ii

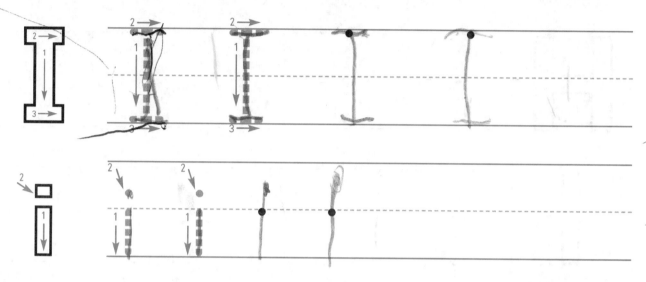

 I and i go together. They are partner letters. Color the two scoops of ice cream in each dish that have partner letters.

14   *Recognizing and writing Ii*

The Letter Jj

 Trace the hollow letters with your finger. Then trace the other letters with a pencil. Now write the letters.

Jj

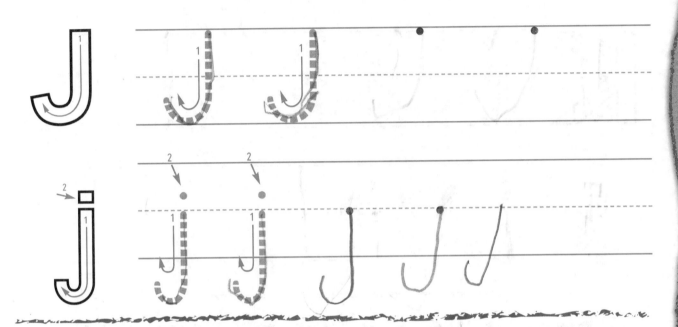

 Draw a line from each picture that has J or j on it to the juggler.

Recognizing and writing **Jj**

The Letter Kk

 Trace the hollow letters with your finger. Then trace the other letters with a pencil. Now write the letters.

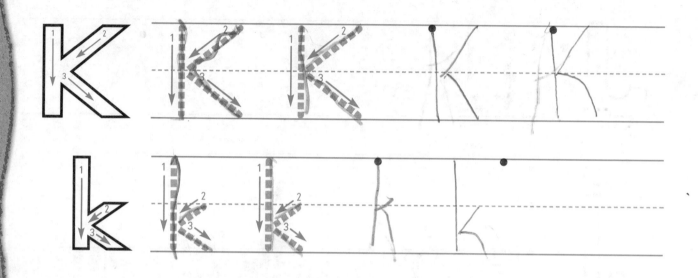

 Draw a line from the kite to each **K** and **k** in the picture.

*Recognizing and writing **Kk***

The Letter Ll

Trace the hollow letters with your finger. Then trace the other letters with a pencil. Now write the letters.

Ll

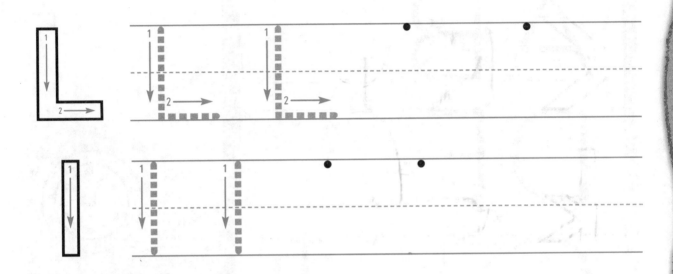

On each log, cross out the letter that is not **L** or **I**.

L K I

d I L

L L A

H L L

C I L

I f I

*Recognizing and writing **Ll***

17

Review A-L

Write the missing letters.

A B C
D E f
G h I
i K L

*Identifying letters of the alphabet **A-L***

Review a-l

Where's the boy sleeping? Draw a line to connect the dots from a to l to find out.

Start

End

*Identifying letters of the alphabet **a-l***

The Letter Mm

 Trace the hollow letters with your finger. Then trace the other letters with a pencil. Now write the letters.

 Mm

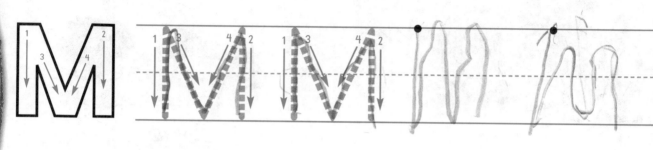

 Help the monkey find his mittens. Follow the letters **M** and **m** to draw a path.

Start

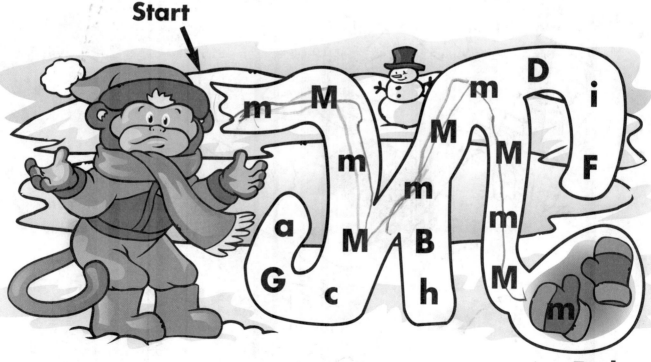

End

20

Recognizing and writing **Mm**

The Letter Nn

Trace the hollow letters with your finger. Then trace the other letters with a pencil. Now write the letters.

 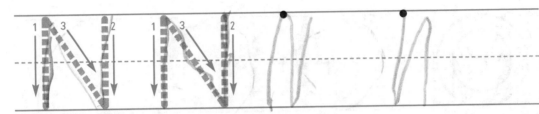

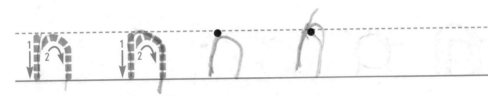

Color the nests that have N or n.

The Letter Oo

Trace the hollow letters with your finger. Then trace the other letters with a pencil. Now write the letters.

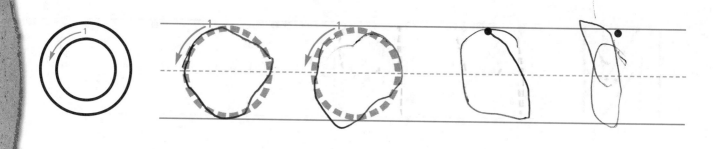

Whooooo is in the tree? Use the color key to find out.

O =    o =

Recognizing and writing Oo

The Letter Pp

 Trace the hollow letters with your finger. Then trace the other letters with a pencil. Now write the letters.

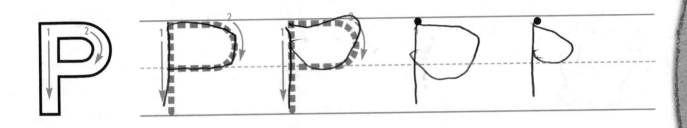

 Circle each penguin that has P or p on it.

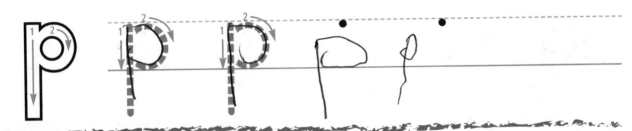

The Letter Qq

 Trace the hollow letters with your finger. Then trace the other letters with a pencil. Now write the letters.

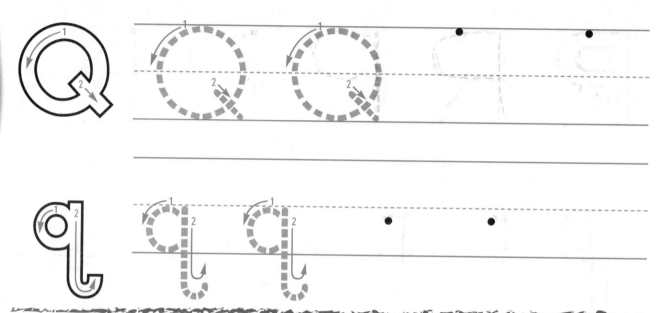

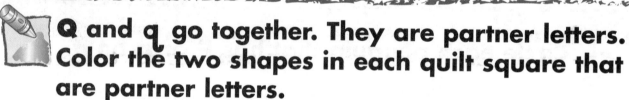 **Q** and **q** go together. They are partner letters. Color the two shapes in each quilt square that are partner letters.

*Recognizing and writing **Qq***

The Letter Rr

 Trace the hollow letters with your finger. Then trace the other letters with a pencil. Now write the letters.

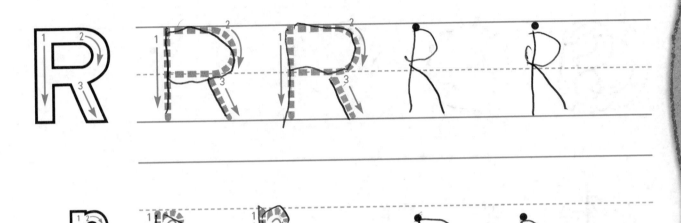

 R and **r** go together. They are partner letters. Color each robot that has partner letters.

The Letter Ss

 Trace the hollow letters with your finger. Then trace the other letters with a pencil. Now write the letters.

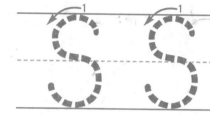

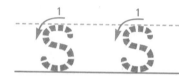

 Find and circle each **S** or **s** in the picture.

*Recognizing and writing **Ss***

The Letter Tt

 Trace the hollow letters with your finger. Then trace the other letters with a pencil. Now write the letters.

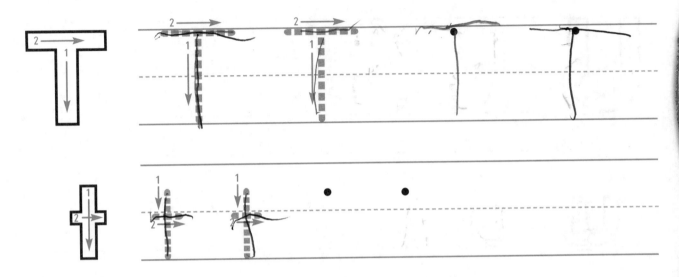

 Draw a line from each toy that has a **T** or **t** on it to the table.

The Letter Uu

 Trace the hollow letters with your finger. Then trace the other letters with a pencil. Now write the letters.

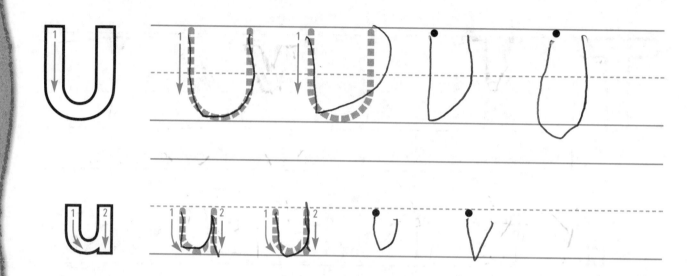

 On each umbrella, cross out the letter that is not **U** or **u**.

28

The Letters Vv and Ww

Trace the hollow letters with your finger.
Then trace the other letters with a pencil.
Now write the letters.

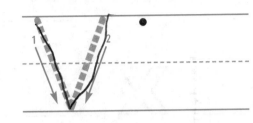

Color each valentine that has **V** or **v** on it.

Now write these letters.

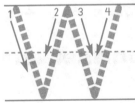

Circle each wagon that has **W** or **w** on it.

The Letters Xx, Yy, and Zz

 Trace the hollow letters with your finger.
Then trace the other letters with a pencil.
Now write the letters.

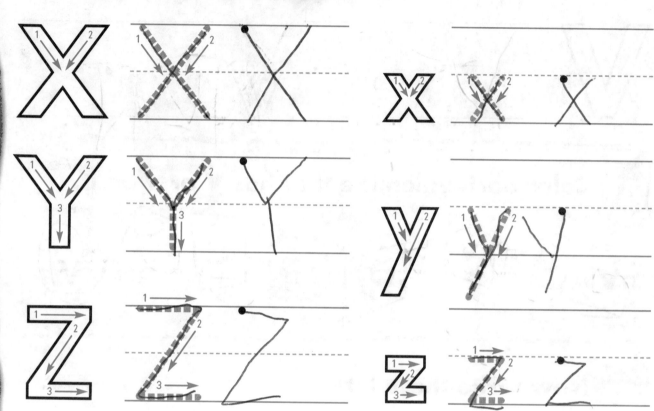

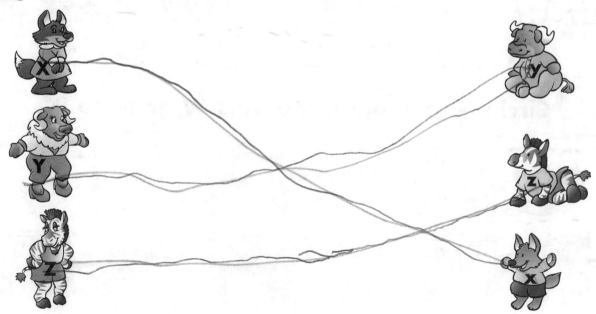 Draw a line between the partner letters.

30

*Recognizing and writing **Xx, Yy, and Zz***

Review A-Z

Write the missing letters.

A B C D E F

G H I J K L

M N O P Q

R S T U V

W X Y Z

Identifying letters of the alphabet A-Z

Review a-z

Where do the old woman and her children live? Draw a line to connect the dots from **a** to **z** to find out.

Identifying letters of the alphabet a-z

Month 2 Checklist

Hands-on activities to help your child in school!

CONSONANTS

Beginning Sounds: pages 35–44, 63

This month your child will learn the sounds of consonants *b, c, f, h, m, n, p, r, t,* and *v* when they appear at the beginning of words. Try the following activities together.

❏ Print the letters *b, c, f, h, m, n, p, r, t,* and *v* on separate index cards. Scatter the cards randomly on the floor. With your child, take turns tossing a button or coin on a letter card, naming the letter, and saying a word that begins with the letter's sound.

❏ Pantomime an action and have your child imitate you. Then have your child guess the action and name the letter that stands for the beginning sound in the action word. For example: *batting, boxing, cutting, combing, fishing, fanning, hopping, hammering, marching, mopping, nailing, nodding, painting, pulling, rowing, running, tapping, tasting, vacuuming.*

❏ Print the letters *b, c, f, h, m, n, p, r, t,* and *v* on separate index cards. Spread the cards on a table. Say a word and have your child find the card that has the letter that stands for the beginning sound in the word. Words you may want to use include the following: *ball, car, fish, hat, mop, net, pig, rake, turtle, valentine.*

VOWELS

Short a: pages 45–46

In Month 2, try any of the activities below to help your child practice identifying the sound of short *a* as in the word *cat.*

❏ Remind your child that *clap* and *hands* have a short *a* sound. Have your child clap his or her hands whenever you say a word that has the sound of short *a.* Then, one at a time, say these words: *cat, pig, mop, man, hat, bag, dad, hen, bug, dance, cap, jet, bat, fan, hot, jam,* and *mat.*

❏ Sit on the floor opposite your child. Say a short *a* word and roll a can to your child. Have your child say a short *a* word and then roll the can back to you. Repeat the activity several times.

WORD FAMILIES

-at, -an: pages 47–62, 64

On the Word Family pages, your child will work with frequently used word endings for the consonant and vowel sounds they have already practiced.

❑ Have your child draw a large cat on a sheet of paper. Work with him or her to draw, or cut out of magazines, pictures with names that rhyme with *cat.* Help your child label each picture.

❑ Write these words on strips of paper, one word per strip, leaving extra space between the letters: *can, fan, man, pan, ran, tan,* and *van.* Help your child cut apart each word in a zigzag pattern between the beginning consonant and the *-an* ending. Then have your child put each puzzle together and read the *-an* word.

Beginning b

 and  begin with
the sound for the letter **b**.

 Name the pictures in each row.
Circle the pictures that start with b.

b

b

 Trace each word. Say the word.

 bell

 bird

 boy

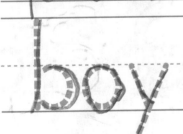 bed

 Answer the riddle with a word you just wrote.

**What has a head and
a foot but no body?**

 Answer the

Recognizing initial consonant **b**

Beginning Hard c

 and begin with the sound for the letter **c**.

Write **c** to make a word that rhymes with the first word in the row. Say the new word.

 rake  <u>c</u>ake

 boat  <u>c</u>oat

 bat  <u>c</u>at

 horn  <u>c</u>orn

Recognizing the hard sound of initial consonant **c**

Beginning f

 and  begin with
the sound for the letter **f**.

**Name each picture.
Write f to finish each word. Say the word.**

fire fan fish five

**Find the pictures of the words you just wrote.
Color them.**

 Find and color 3 more pictures that start with f.

Beginning h

and 🥧 begin with the sound for the letter **h.**

**Name the pictures in each row.
Circle the pictures that start with h.**

Trace each word. Say the word.

harp

hen

horse

hat

Recognizing initial consonant **h**

Beginning m

 and  begin with the sound for the letter **m**.

Name each picture.
Write **m** to finish each word. Say the word.

 an

 ilk

 ice

mask

 oon

 op

Write **m** beside each picture that starts with **m**.

Beginning n

 and  begin with the sound for the letter **n**.

 Find and color 7 things that begin with n.

 Trace each word. Say the word.

 nine

 nut

*Recognizing initial consonant **n***

Beginning p

 and  begin with
the sound for the letter **p**.

 Write **p** to finish each word.
Find the pictures that show the words.
Color them. Say the words.

__p__ig

__p__ien

__p__iano

__p__illow

__p__ail

Recognizing initial consonant **p**

Beginning r

 and  begin with
the sound for the letter **r**.

 Name each picture.
Color the pictures that start with r.

Write r beside each picture that starts with r.

 rake

 rig

 mat

 noz

*Recognizing initial consonant **r***

Beginning t

 and begin with the sound for the letter **t**.

Name the pictures in each row.
Circle the pictures that start with **t**.

Trace each word. Say the word.

10 ten   tie

turtle   table

*Recognizing initial consonant **t***

Beginning v

 and begin with the sound for the letter **v**.

 Find and color 7 things that begin with v.

 Trace each word. Say the word.

van   violin

Recognizing initial consonant **v**

Hats Off for a

The word h**a**t has the short **a** sound.

 Say each picture name.
Circle the picture if you hear the short **a** sound.

*Recognizing the short vowel sound of **a***

Short a

  **Write a to finish each word.
Read the word.**

m __a__ n   g   s   j   m

 **Say each picture name.
Write the word.**

 c a t    c a n

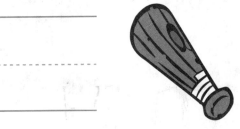

Recognizing and writing words with the short sound of a

Words With at

The word c<u>at</u>  ends with the sounds for the letters **at**.

cat

 Say each picture name. Read the word below it. Circle **at** in each word.

rat   **hat**   **bat**

 Say the words. Trace the letters **at**. Say the sounds at the end of each word.

cat   mat

Recognizing words with -at

More Words With at

Say the names of the pictures in each row.
Circle the pictures with names that have the
same ending sounds.

 **cat**  **bat**  **cake** **hat**

 **hat**  **ham**  **mat**  **rat**

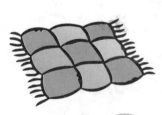 **mat**  **cat**   **bat**  **moon**

 **bat**  **bee**  **hat**  **cat**

Recognizing words with -at

Rhyme Time

 and have the same ending sounds.

 and  rhyme.

h<u>at</u>   c<u>at</u>

 Say the picture names.
Read the rhyming words next to them.
Trace the first letter in each word.

 bat    hat

---

 Read the rhyming words. Trace the first
letter in each word. Then circle the
fat cat.

fat cat

Recognizing words with -at

Match Them Up!

 **Read the rhyming words.
Then color the pictures.**

mat   **cat**   **hat**   **bat**

 **Say each word. Then trace the
beginning letter. Draw a line to each
matching picture.**

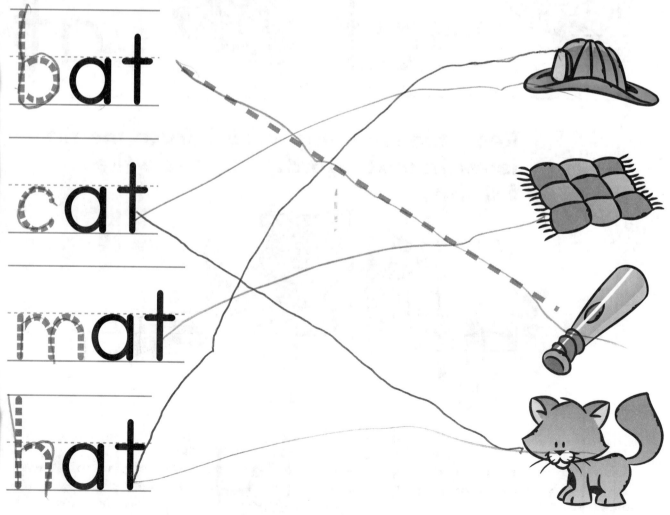

bat

cat

mat

hat

Recognizing words with -at

Play concentration!

fat	**fat**
cat	**cat**
bat	**bat**
rat	**rat**

Parents: Play concentration with two players. First cut apart the cards and place face down. The first player turns over two cards and reads each word aloud. If they match, the player wins the pair. If not, the cards are turned facedown and it's the second player's turn. The player with the most word pairs wins.

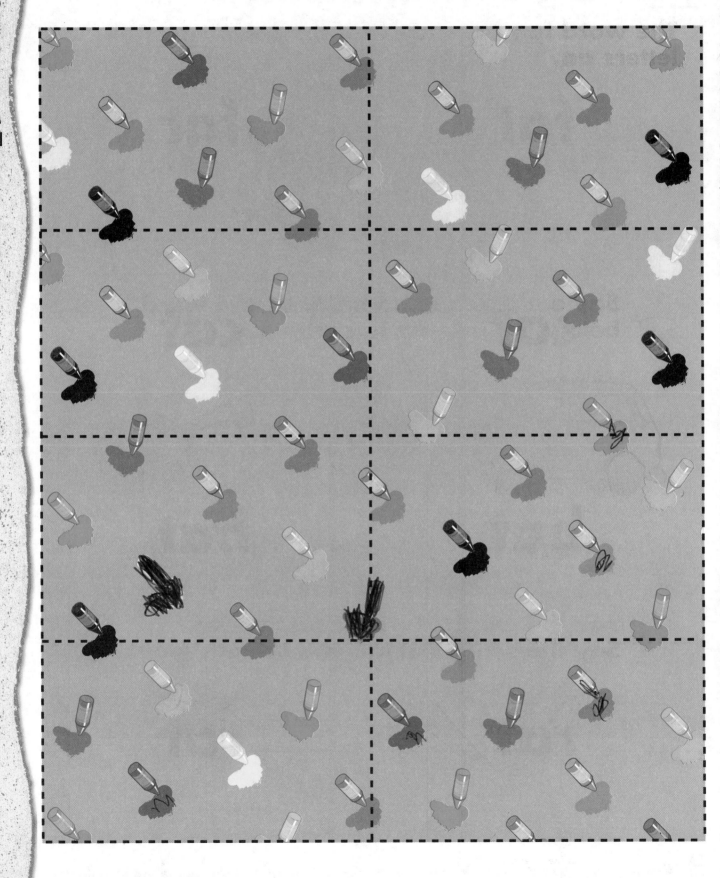

Matching words with **-at**

Words With an

The word **fan**  ends with the sounds for the letters **an**.

fan

 Say each picture name. Read the word below it. Circle **an** in each word.

van   **man**   **p**an

 Say the words. Trace the letters **an**. Say the sounds at the end of each word.

Recognizing words with -an

53

More Words With an

Say the names of the pictures in each row. Circle the pictures with names that have the same ending sounds.

fan **foot** **can** **tan**

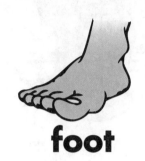   

man **van** **mop** **pan**

can **fan** **man** **cake**

pan **can** **pig** **van**

Recognizing words with -an

Rhyme Time

 and have the same ending sounds.

 and  rhyme.

man

fan

 Say the picture names.
Read the rhyming words next to them.
Trace the first letter in each word.

 **can**  **man**

 Read the rhyming words.
Trace the first letter in each word.
Then circle the **tan van**.

 **tan**  **van**

*Recognizing words with **-an***

Match Them Up!

Read the rhyming words.
Then color the pictures.

pan   **can**   **van**   **fan**

   Say each word.
Then trace the beginning letter.
Draw a line to each matching picture.

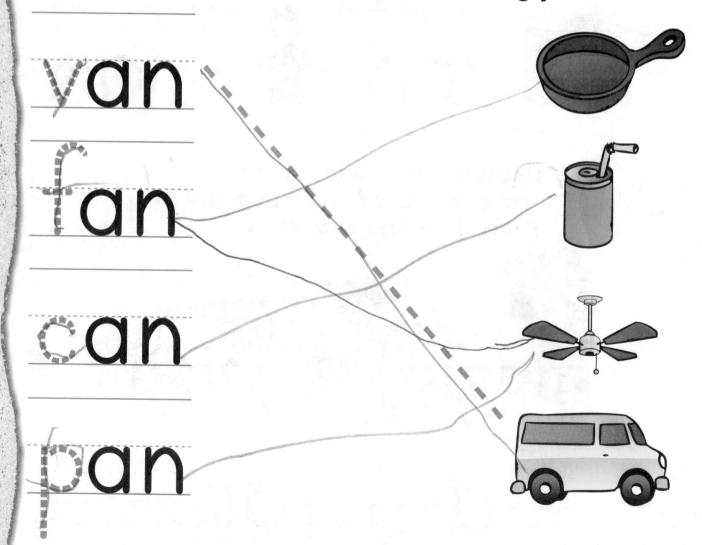

van

fan

can

pan

Recognizing words with -an

Play concentration!

fan	**fan**
can	**can**
pan	**pan**
man	**man**

Parents: Play concentration with two players. First cut apart the cards and place face down. The first player turns over two cards and reads each word aloud. If they match, the player wins the pair. If not, the cards are turned facedown and it's the second player's turn. The player with the most word pairs wins.

57

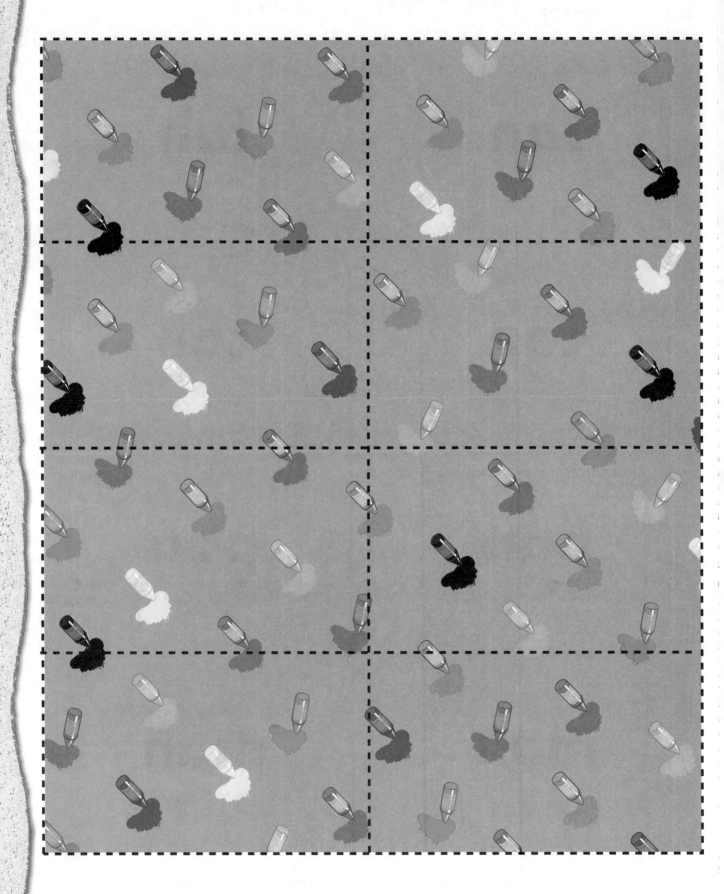

Matching words with **-an**

Parents: Remove pages 59-62 from this book. See directions for making mini storybooks on the inside of the front cover.

CAT MAN

But one thing Cat Man does not have—RATS!

This is Cat Man and his
cats, cats, cats.

Cat Man has cats with fans
and cats with hats.

Cat Man has tan cats . . . .

Cat Man has cats in pots and pans.

and fat cats.

Cats on mats.
Cats in cans.

Practice Test

Say the picture name. Fill in the circle next to the letter that stands for the beginning sound.

○ b
● r
○ t

⊗ c
⊗ p
● f

● m
⊗ b
⊗ t

⊗ h
● v
○ b

⊗ c
⊗ n
● h

● n
● f
○ t

⊗ m
● b
⊗ h

● t
⊗ c
⊗ r

● f
○ n
○ b

⊗ c
⊗ r
● p

○ v
○ n
● r

○ b
● c
⊗ v

Recognizing initial consonant sounds

Practice Test

**Say the picture names in each row.
Fill in the circles below the two pictures with
names that rhyme.**

○ **cat**   ○ **cap**   ○ **hat**   ○ **can**

● **man**   ○ **pig**   ● **mop**   ● **pan**

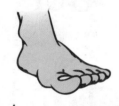   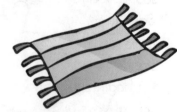

○ **foot**   ○ **hat**   ● **can**   ○ **mat**

○ **van**   ○ **five**   ○ **fan**   ○ **top**

● **bat**   ● **mat**   ● **ham**   ○ **bell**

Recognizing words with -at and -an

Month 3 Checklist

Hands-on activities to help your child in school!

CONSONANTS

Beginning Sounds: pages 67-76, 95

This month, your child will continue to learn the sounds of consonants that appear at the beginning of words. In addition to reviewing letters already introduced, your child will practice hard sounds represented by the letters *g, j, k, l,* and *w.*

❑ Complete the worksheets.

❑ Give your child five sheets of heavy paper, magazines, child safety-scissors, and paste or glue. Have your child print the letters *g, j, k, l,* and *w* at the top of each page, one letter per page. Work together to find and cut out pictures with names that begin with each of the letters. Consider doing one letter per work period. If your child cuts out pictures with names beginning with *c* instead of *k,* it may be a good time to mention that there are two spellings for the /k/ sound: *k* and *c.* When you are finished, clip or staple the pages together to make a letter book.

❑ Say the names of people, one at a time, that begin with *g, j, k, l,* and *w,* such as *Gabe, Jesse, Katie, Lindsay, and Winnie.* After you say each name, have your child write the letter that stands for the beginning sound. Then ask your child to say other names with the same letter at the beginning. You may want to repeat the activity with other categories, such as *things in school, toys and games, or animals.*

❑ Write the letters *g, j, k, l,* and *w* on each side of a cube-shaped tissue box, one letter per side. With your child, take turns tossing the box and naming a word that begins with the letter that lands faceup.

VOWELS

Short e: pages 77, 78, 96

Try any of the activities below to help your child practice identifying the sound of short *e* as in the word *hen*.

❏ Complete the worksheets.

❏ Have your child draw pictures of these short *e* words on heavy paper, one per sheet: *hen, jet, bed, web,* and *net.* Help your child label each of the drawings with large print. Then have him or her trace over the letter *e* in each word with glue. Cover the glue with glitter, sand, rice, beans, or yarn. When the glue dries, have your child trace the letter *e* with a finger as he or she reads the word.

❏ First, explain that the word *jet* has the sound of short *e* in the middle. Then say, "Fly like a jet whenever you hear me say a word that has the sound of short *e*." One at a time, say these words: *men, tag, wet, wig, red, man, pet, rug, pen, lid, bed,* and *beg.*

WORD FAMILIES

-et, -en: pages 79-94

Use these activities to help your child understand word families.

❏ Complete the worksheets.

❏ Write these word endings on strips of paper, one per strip: *-et* and *-en.* Write these letters on small squares of paper, one per square: *b, g, h, j, l, m, n, p, t, v,* and *w.* Have your child choose a letter and place it in front of a word ending. Take turns reading the words your child builds. Together, decide if each one is or is not a "real" word.

❏ Ask your child to think of a word that begins with *n* and rhymes with *get.* Have your child say *net-get.* Then ask for a word that:
  • begins with *t* and rhymes with *Ben (ten-Ben)*
  • begins with *m* and rhymes with *pet (met-pet)*
  • begins with *p* and rhymes with *men (pen-men)*

Review Beginning Sounds
b, f, h, and t

**Say the name of each picture.
Then say the sound of each letter.
Color the picture if its name begins
with that letter sound.**

*Reviewing initial consonants **b, f, h, t***

Review Beginning Sounds
c, m, n, and r

 Color the pictures that begin with the sound of—

c= m= n= r=

 You have made a pretty  rug.

*Reviewing initial consonants **c, m, n, r***

Review Beginning Sounds
b, n, t, and v

**Say the sound of each letter.
Then say each picture name.
Draw a line from each letter to the picture
that's name begins with that letter sound.**

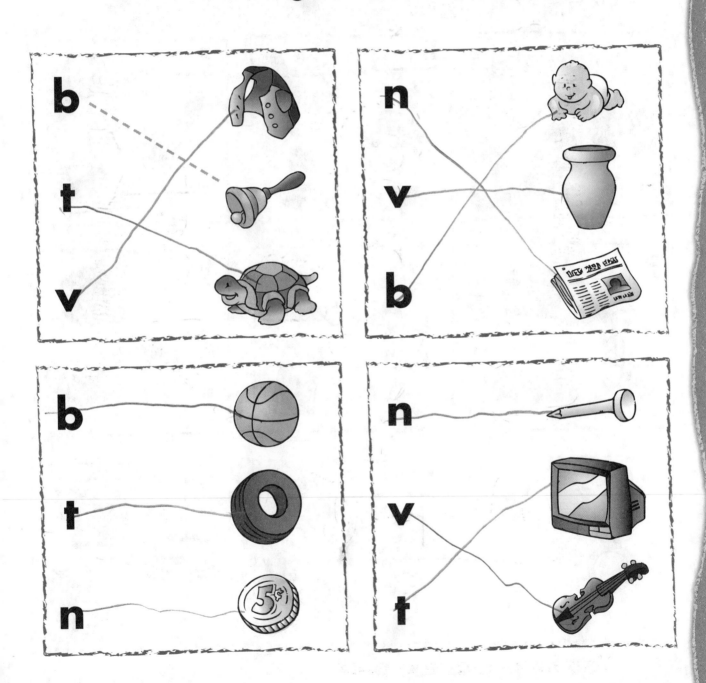

Review Beginning Sounds
c, f, h, and p

Say the sound of each letter. Then say each picture name. Circle the picture that's name begins with that letter sound.

Reviewing initial consonants c, f, h, p

Review Beginning Sounds
m, p, r, and v

Say each picture name.
Find the letter in the box that
stands for the beginning sound.
Write the letter on the line.

| m | p | r | v |

pig   mat   vest

red   Pie   mop

 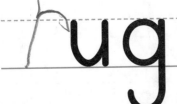 

van   rug   man

---

*Reviewing initial consonants **m, p, r, v***

Beginning Hard g

 and **begin with the hard sound of the letter g.**

 Name each picture. Draw lines from the  **to the pictures that start with g.**

 Look at each picture. Write a word that starts with g to finish each rhyme.

a _____ **in a coat**

a loose _____

Recognizing the hard sound of initial consonant **g**

Beginning j

 and  **begin with the sound for the letter j.**

 **Name each picture.
Circle the pictures with names that start with j.**

Write j to make a word that rhymes with the first one.

net

_____et

ham

_____am

Recognizing initial consonant j

Beginning k

 and begin with
the sound for the letter **k.**

Name each picture.
Write **k** to finish each word. Say the word.

Key   Kite   King

Find the pictures of the words you just wrote.
Color them.

Find and color 2 more pictures that start with **k.**

*Recognizing initial consonant **k***

Beginning l

 and begin with
the sound for the letter **l**.

Write **l** to finish each word.
Find the pictures that show the words.
Color them. Then say the words.

l og

l eaf

l amb

l ock

l adder

Beginning w

 and  begin with the sound for the letter **w**.

 Name the pictures in each row.
Circle the pictures that start with w.

W

W

 **Look at each picture.**
Trace a word that starts with w to finish each rhyme.

 a pig in a ___wig___

 a dragon in a ___wagon___

Recognizing initial consonant **w**

Short e Riddle

The word h<u>e</u>n has the short e sound.

 **Say each picture name.
Color the space if you hear the short e sound.**

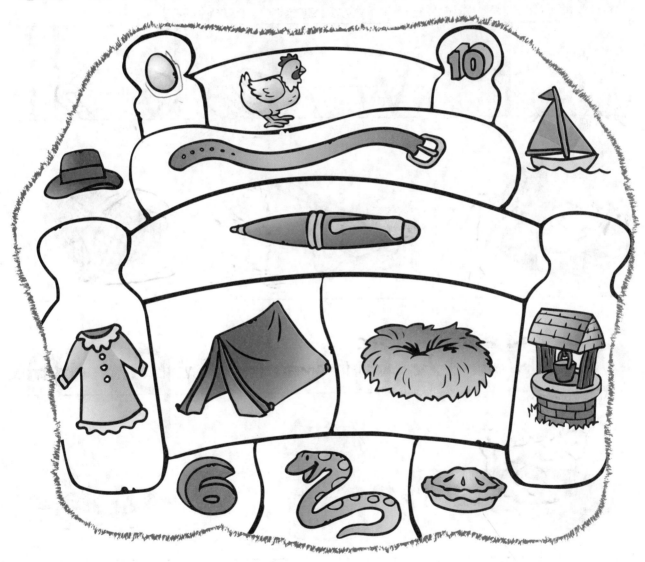

What has four legs but cannot run? a _____

Riddle answer: a bed

Short e

**Write e to finish each word.
Read the word.**

j e t   w   b   b   ll

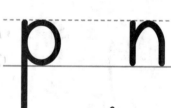

h   n   n   t   p   n

s   l d   w   ll   w   t

Recognizing and writing words with the short sound of e

Words With et

The word j<u>et</u> ends with the sounds for the letters **et**.

 **jet**

 Say each picture name. Read the word below it. Circle **et** in each word.

w(et)

net

pet

 Say the words. Trace the letters **et**. Say the sounds at the end of each word.

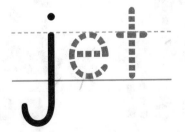

jet

net

More Words With et

 Say the names of the pictures in each row. Circle the pictures with names that have the same ending sounds.

 **net**    **pet**    **nest**    **wet**

 **pet**    **pig**    **net**    **jet**

 **jet**    **jar**    **wet**    **pet**

 **wet**    **net**    **well**    **pet**

Recognizing words with -et

Rhyme Time

 and have the same ending sounds.
 and rhyme.

net

jet

 Say the picture names. Read the rhyming words below them. Trace the first letter in each word.

net   jet

 Read the rhyming words. Trace the first letter in each word. Then circle the wet pet.

wet pet

Match Them Up!

**Read the rhyming words.
Then color the pictures.**

net　　**jet**　　**wet**　　**pet**

  **Say each word. Then trace the
beginning letter. Draw a line to
each matching picture.**

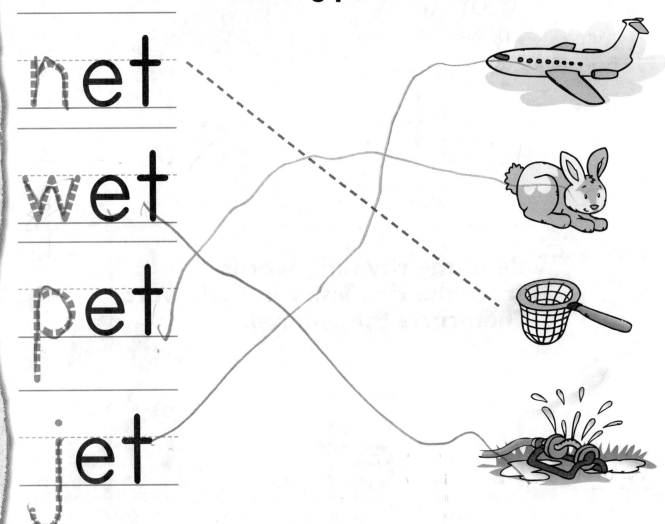

net

wet

pet

jet

Recognizing words with -et

Play concentration!

net	**net**
pet	**pet**
jet	**jet**
wet	**wet**

Parents: Play concentration with two players. First cut apart the cards and place facedown. The first player turns over two cards and reads each word aloud. If they match, the player wins the pair. If not, the cards are turned face down and it's the second player's turn. The player with the most word pairs wins.

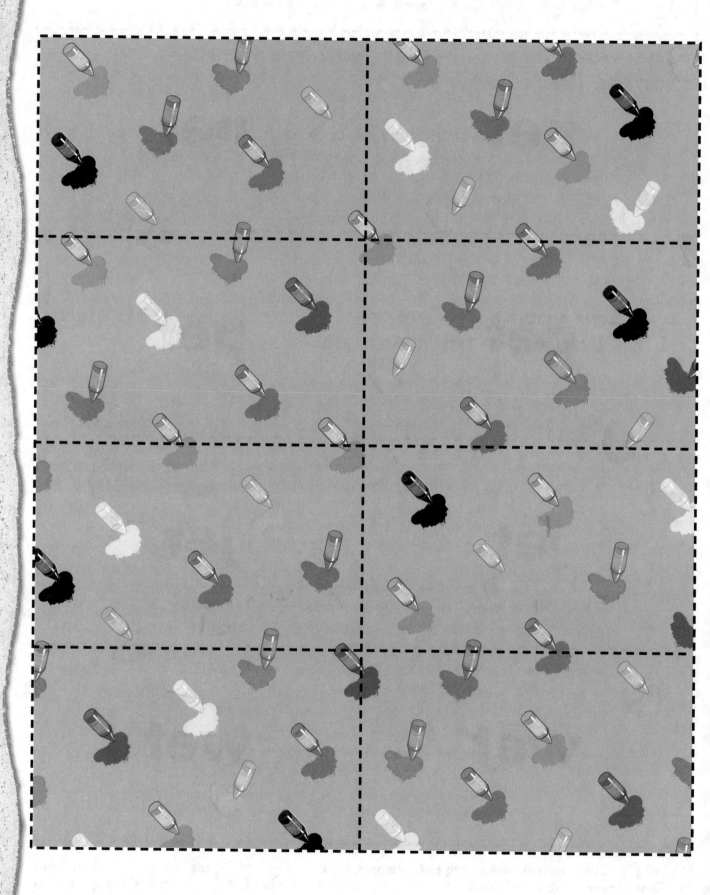

Recognizing words with **-et**

Words With en

The word h<u>en</u>  ends with the sounds for the letters **en**.

hen

 Say each picture name. Read the word below it. Circle **en** in each word.

pen   ten   men

 Say the words. Trace the letters **en**. Say the sounds at the end of each word.

 hen    ten

---

Recognizing words with -en

More Words With en

Say the names of the pictures in each row. Circle the pictures with names that have the same ending sounds.

 **pen**  **men**  **pet**  **ten**

 **men**  **map**  **ten**  **hen**

 **hen**  **pen**  **hat**  **men**

 **ten**  **hen**  **pen** **top**

Recognizing words with -en

Rhyme Time

 and  have the same ending sounds.

and rhyme.

p<u>en</u> **h<u>en</u>**

 Say the picture names. Read the rhyming words next to them. Trace the first letter in each word.

 **hen**  **pen**

 Read the rhyming words.
Trace the first letter in each word.
Then circle the **ten men**.

**ten** **men**

Recognizing words with **-en**

Match Them Up!

**Read the rhyming words.
Then color the pictures.**

hen   **pen**   **ten**   **men**

**Say each word.
Then trace the beginning letter.
Draw a line to each matching picture.**

pen

ten

hen

men

*Recognizing words with **-en***

Play concentration!

pen	pen
men	men
ten	ten
hen	hen

Parents: Play concentration with two players. First cut apart the cards and place face down. The first player turns over two cards and reads each word aloud. If they match, the player wins the pair. If not, the cards are turned face down and it's the second player's turn. The player with the most word pairs wins.

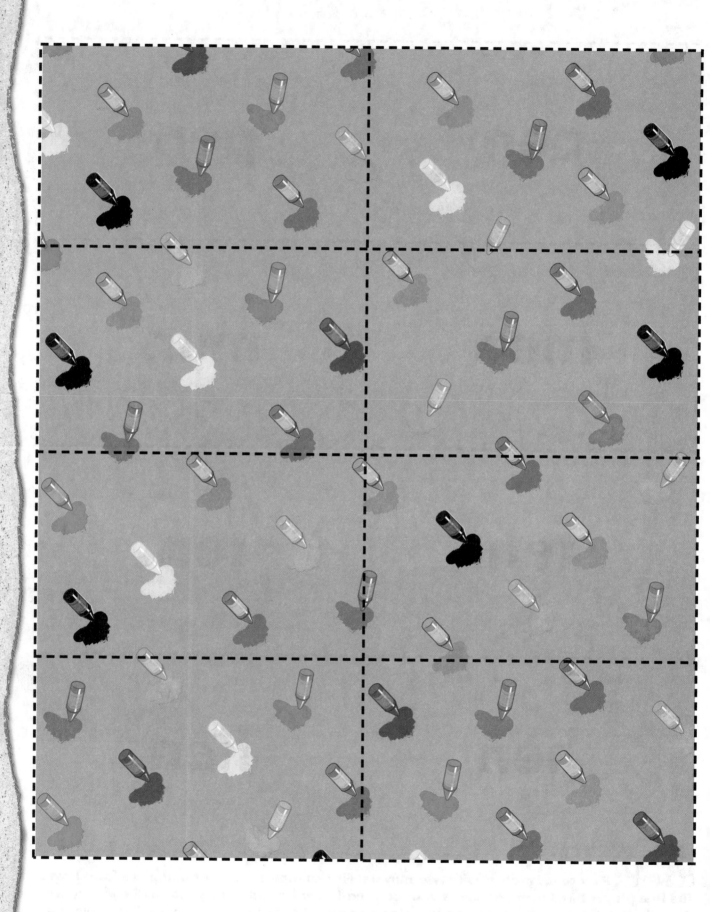

*Recognizing words with **-en***

MY WET HEN

This is Ben...

This is Ben,
his wet hen,
and a wet Ken!

and his pet hen.

and his wet hen.

This is Ken.

This is Ben . . . .

Look out, Ben!

Look out for Ken!

Practice Test: Beginning Sounds

 Say the sound of the letter at the beginning of the row. Then say each picture name. Fill in the circle if the picture name begins with that letter.

Recognizing initial consonant sounds

Practice Test: Short a and Short e

Say the picture name.
Fill in the circle next to the correct word.

○ hat
● hen

○ bag
● beg

○ cot
● cat

● ham
○ hem

○ nap
● net

● red
○ rag

○ pan
● pen

○ bat
● bed

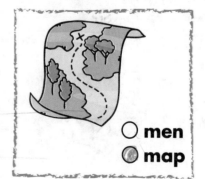
● hat
○ hot

○ pen
● pan

○ ten
● tag

○ men
● map

*Recognizing words with short **a** and short **e***

Month 4 Checklist

Hands-on activities to help your child in school!

CONSONANTS

Beginning Sounds: pages 99-108, 127
This month, your child will continue to learn the sounds of consonants that appear at the beginning of words, especially the sounds made by the letters *d, q, s, y,* and *z.* Use any of the activities below to help him or her recognize the sounds these initial consonants make:

❑ Complete the worksheets.

❑ Ask your child to make the sound that a duck makes. Point out that *duck* begins with the letter *d* and *quack* begins with the letter *q.* Then say, "Listen to these words and quack when you hear one that begins with the letter *d.*" Say a list of words—some of which begin with *d.* Repeat this activity for words that begin with *y, q, z,* and *s.* (With the initial *s* words, be careful to avoid words such as *cents* that begin with the soft *c* sound.)

❑ Cut a big letter *y* from a sheet of yellow paper. Go on a yellow hunt with your child. When your child finds something that is yellow, ask him or her to hold up the letter *y* and say "yellow!"

❑ If practical, pay a visit to a zoo and look for animals with names that begin with *d, q, s, y,* and *z.*

VOWELS

Short *i*: pages 109-110, 128
This month, your child will also practice the short *i* vowel sound, as heard in the word *pig.*

❑ Complete the worksheets.

❑ Play "Listen and Spin." Ask your child to listen carefully as you say a list of words. When a word with the short *i* sound, such as *spin*, is said, he or she should spin like a top. Include these short *i* words in your list: *pig, big, win, pin, fish, kick,* and *mitt.*

❑ Play "I Wish." Point out that *wish* has the short *i* sound. Say, "I wish I had a . . . pig!" Then challenge your child to wish for something that's name contains the short *i* sound. Take turns making up "I wish. . ." sentences.

WORD FAMILIES

-in, -ig: pages 111-126

Your child has already learned the sounds of the consonants that begin words. It is now important for him or her to learn about common word endings for those beginning sounds.

❏ Complete the worksheets.

❏ Play "Word Family Tongue Twisters." Write the word ending *-in* on a piece of paper. Challenge your child to repeat this sentence three times: *I grin when I win, then I touch my chin.* Do the same for the word ending *-ig* and the tongue twister: *The pig with the wig danced a silly little jig.*

❏ Read aloud one of your child's favorite books, and encourage him or her to point out words that end in *-in* and *-ig.*

Review Beginning Sounds
b, k, n

 Name the first picture in each row. Circle the picture that starts with the same sound.

 Name each picture. Write b, k, or n to finish each word.

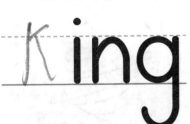

King Bug nest

Review Beginning Sounds
f, g, t

 Say each picture name.
Circle the letter that says its beginning sound.

f d	d g	t h	b g
g b	f s	t w	f h
r t	g m	k f	t s
g r	d f	g y	l t

 **Color the pictures that begin with the sound of t.**

*Reviewing initial consonants **f, g, t***

Review Beginning Sounds
h, m, p

Say the sound of each letter.
Circle the pictures that start with that sound.

h

m

p

Find 4 pictures of words that begin with the sound of p. Color them.

Reviewing initial consonants h, m, p

Say the first word in the row.
Change one letter to make a word that rhymes.
Write l, r, or w to finish each word.

cake   ake   ake

sock   ock   ock

king   ing   ing

Review Beginning Sounds
c, j, v

  Look at the picture.
Write c, j, or v to finish each word.

ˌcake   ˌcookies   ˌeil

ˌet   ˌat   ˌelly

ˌest   ˌandle   ˌug

Reviewing initial consonants c, j, v

103

Beginning d

 and begin with the sound for the letter **d**.

 Name each picture. Draw lines from the  to the pictures that start with **d**.

Trace each word. Say the word.

duck   doll

*Recognizing initial consonant **d***

Beginning q

 and  begin with the sound for the letter q.

 Name each picture. Draw lines from the  to the pictures that start with q.

 Trace each word. Say the word.

 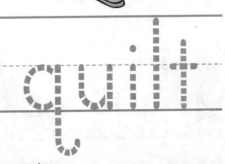

queen   quilt

Beginning s

 and begin with the sound for the letter **s**.

 Name each picture.
Write s to finish each word. Say the word.

s aw

___ un

___ ail

___ ock

___ ix

___ ink

 **Write s by the pictures that start with s.**

 _____

 _____

_____

Recognizing initial consonant **s**

Beginning y

 and  begin with the sound for the letter y.

 Trace each word. Say the word.

yard yawn yarn

Circle the correct answer.

What goes up and down but never gives you a ride?

CONSONANTS

Beginning z

 begins with the sound for the letter **z**.

 **Name each picture.
Color the pictures that start with z.**

 Trace each word. Say the word.

 zebra   zipper

108

Recognizing initial consonant z

Listen for Short i

The word pin has the short i sound.

 Say each picture name.
Do you hear the short i sound?

Color **if you do. Color** **if you do not.**

Short i

Say each picture name. Circle the picture with the short i sound in its name. Write i to finish each word. Trace the word.

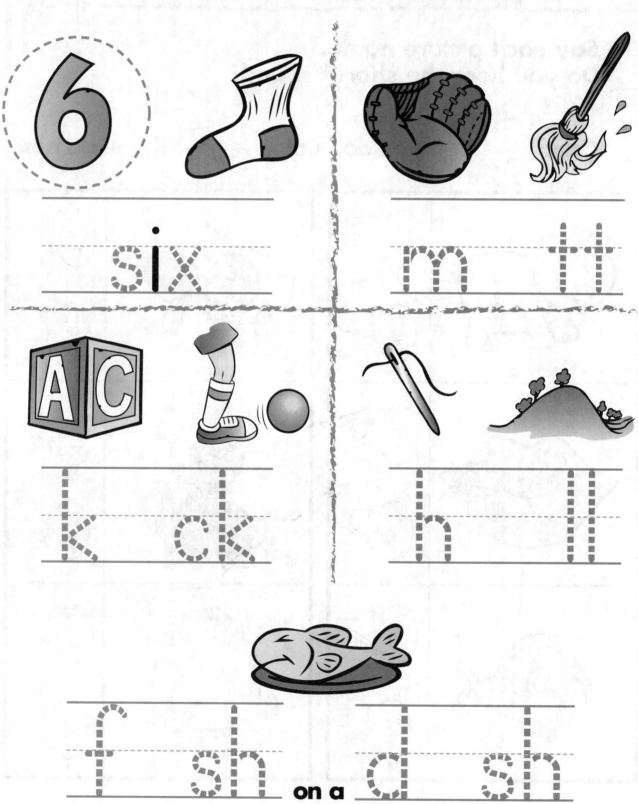

s i x   m __ tt

k __ ck   h __ ll

f __ sh **on a** d __ sh

*Recognizing and writing words with the short sound of **i***

Words with in

pin

The word **p<u>in</u>** ends with the sounds for the letters **in**.

Say each picture name. Read the word below it. Circle **in** in each word.

ch(in)   **grin**   **fin**

Say the words. Trace the letters **in**. Say the sounds at the end of each word.

pin   **thin**

Recognizing words with -in

More Words with in

 Say the names of the pictures in each row.
Circle the pictures with names that have the same
ending sounds.

fin **pin** **frog** **chin**

pin **chin** **fin** **pot**

chin **chick** **fin** **grin**

grin **pin** **green** **chin**

*Recognizing words with **-in***

Rhyme Time

 and have the same ending sounds.
 and  rhyme.

chin →    **pin**

 Say the picture names and read the rhyming words. Trace the first letter in each word.

f in   **p in**

  Read the rhyming words. Trace the first letters in each word. Then circle the thin pin.

thin pin

Match Them Up!

 Read the rhyming words.

pin　　　**fin**　　　**grin**　　　**chin**

  Say each word. Then trace the beginning letters. Draw a line to each matching picture.

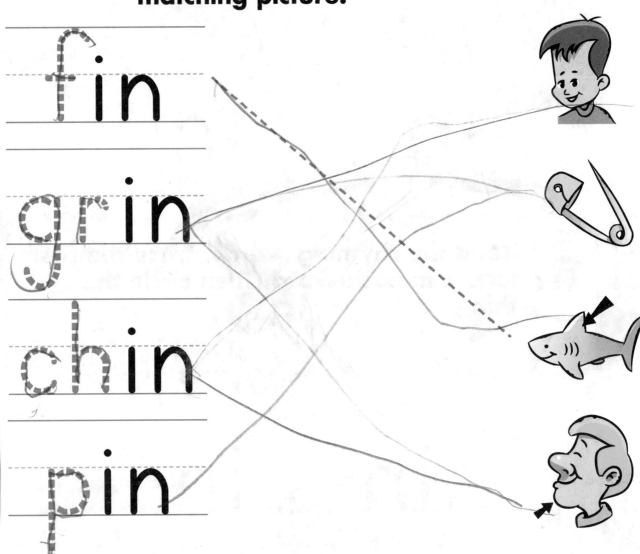

fin

grin

chin

pin

Play concentration!

pin	**pin**
fin	**fin**
grin	**grin**
chin	**chin**

Parents: Play concentration with two players. First cut apart the cards and place facedown. The first player turns over two cards and reads each word aloud. If they match, the player wins the pair. If not, the cards are turned facedown and it's the second player's turn. The player with the most word pairs wins.

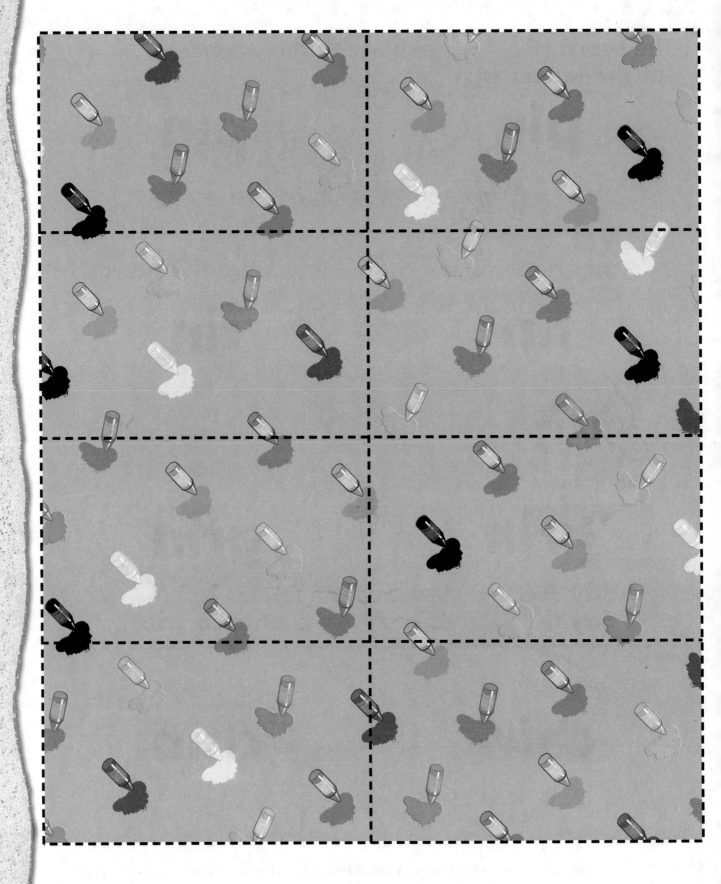

Recognizing words with **-in**

Words with ig

The word **pig** ends with the sounds for the letters **ig**.

pig

Say each picture name and read the word.
Circle **ig** in each word.

wig   **jig**   **dig**

Say the words. Trace the letters **ig**.
Say the sounds at the end of each word.

pig   twig

Recognizing words with -ig

More Words with ig

 Say the names of the pictures in each row. Circle the pictures with names that have the same ending sounds.

wig   **pig**   **twig**   **witch**

jig   **wig**   **jump**   **twig**

pig   **pie**   **wig**   **jig**

twig   **pig**   **twins**   **dig**

Recognizing words with -ig

Rhyme Time

 and  have the same ending sounds.
 and  rhyme.

dig    **pig**

 Say the picture names and read the rhyming words. Trace the first letter in each word.

   dig      wig

 Read the rhyming words.
Trace the first letter in each word.
Then circle the big pig.

big

pig

Match Them Up!

 Read the rhyming words.

pig   **wig**   **jig**   **twig**

  Say each word. Then trace the beginning letter. Draw a line to each matching picture.

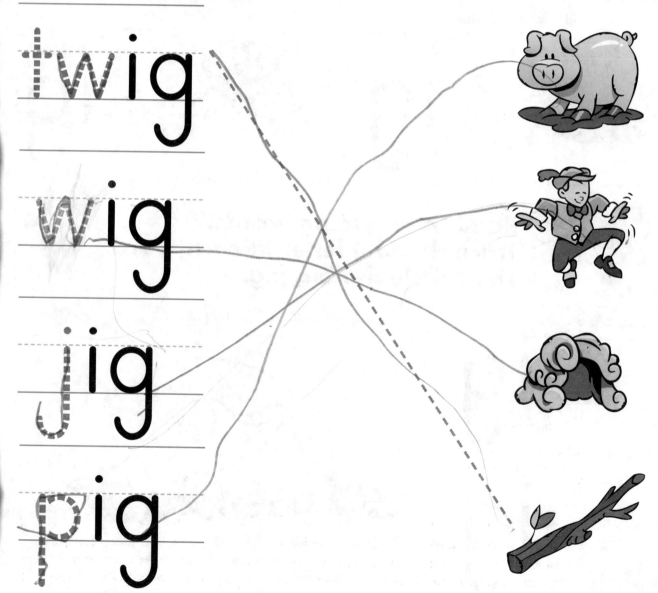

twig

wig

jig

pig

Recognizing words with -ig

Play concentration!

big	**big**
twig	**twig**
wig	**wig**
pig	**pig**

Parents: Play concentration with two players. First cut apart the cards and place facedown. The first player turns over two cards and reads each word aloud. If they match, the player wins the pair. If not, the cards are turned face down and it's the second player's turn. The player with the most word pairs wins.

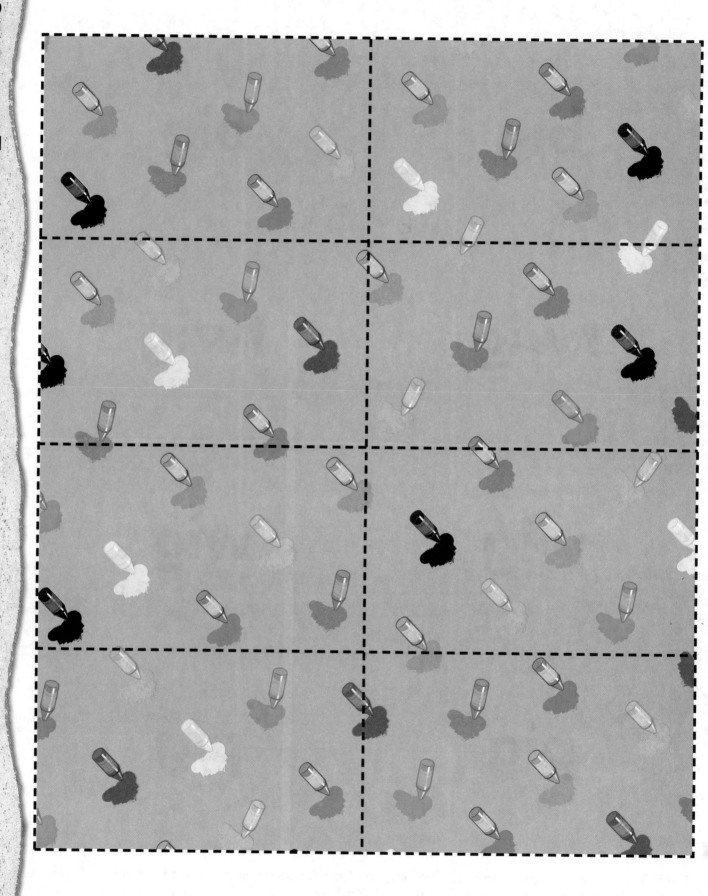

*Recognizing words with **-ig***

Thin Pig has a big grin!
It can be good to be thin!

Thin Pig.

Thin Pig did not win.

Big Pig.

Big Pig wins.

Thin Pig is thin,
thin, thin!

Big Pig is big,
big, big!

Practice Test

 Name each picture. Fill in the circle next to the letter for the beginning sound.

- ○ m
- ● t
- ○ r

- ○ n
- ○ p
- ● d

- ● r
- ○ f
- ○ l

- ● n
- ○ k
- ○ p

- ○ c
- ● s
- ○ w

- ○ x
- ○ q
- ● z

- ● g
- ○ v
- ○ w

- ○ s
- ○ k
- ● b

- ○ t
- ● m
- ○ j

- ○ j
- ● h
- ○ y

- ● p
- ○ d
- ○ f

- ○ s
- ○ y
- ● l

Recognizing initial consonant sounds

Practice Test

Say the picture name.
Fill in the circle next to the correct word.

- ● bag
- ○ bed
- ○ big

- ● gas
- ○ get
- ○ girl

- ○ hat
- ● hen
- ○ hill

- ○ pan
- ○ peg
- ● pig

- ○ nag
- ● net
- ○ nip

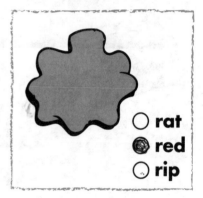
- ○ rat
- ● red
- ○ rip

- ○ bat
- ○ beg
- ● bib

- ○ pat
- ● pen
- ○ pin

- ○ wag
- ○ web
- ● wig

- ○ lad
- ○ leg
- ● lid

- ● cat
- ○ cot
- ○ cut

- ● ham
- ○ hem
- ○ him

*Recognizing words with short **a**, **e**, and **i***

Month 5 Checklist

Hands-on activities to help your child in school!

CONSONANTS

Review Beginning Sounds: pages 131-133, 159
Ending Sounds: pages 134-137
For this month, your child will begin to learn the sounds of consonants at the end of words, especially the sounds made by final *d, g, n, t, p, x,* and *b.*

❑ Complete the worksheets.
❑ Play a rhyming game with your child. Say a one-syllable word that ends in *d, g, n, t, p, x, b,* or *m.* Challenge your child to think of a word that rhymes. For example, *big/wig, box/fox,* and so on.
❑ Write the word *mom* on a piece of paper and have your child read it aloud. Ask what letter is used twice in the word. Repeat this for the words *pop, tot, bib,* and *pup.*

BLENDS & DIGRAPHS

bl, cl, fl, gl, pl, sl: pages 138-140
Blends are letter combinations that combine their sounds. For example, the word *flap* begins with the blend *fl.* When you say it, you can hear the *f* and the *l* working together to form a new sound.
The following activities will help your child understand blends *bl, cl, fl, gl, pl,* and *sl.*

❑ Complete the worksheets.
❑ On a sheet of paper, write *bl* in blue crayon. Have your child say the color name. Point out that the word *blue* begins with the letters *bl.* Challenge your child to go around your home and hold up the "blue card" next to blue things, saying *blue* each time.
❑ Read aloud a picture book and ask your child to point out words that begin with *bl, cl, fl, gl, pl,* and *sl.*
❑ Write the letters *b, c, f, g, p, s,* and *l* on index cards. Turn all the cards letter-side down, except for the *l* card. Flip over a card and say a word beginning with the letter on the card followed by *l.* (For example, if you turn over *b,* you might say *black.*) Take turns flipping cards until all the cards have been used.

Short o: pages 141-142, 160

This month, your child will also practice the short o vowel sound, as heard in the word *top*.

❏ Complete the worksheets.

❏ Write *dog* on a sheet of paper and ask your child to read it. Point out the short o sound. Say, "Listen carefully to these words. If I say a word with the short o sound, bark like a dog." Then say a list of words that includes these short o entries: *top, log, mom, lots, stop, drop,* and *hog.*

❏ Say the words *top* and *bottom*, explaining that both have the short o sound. Ask your child to point out things in the house that are on *top* of and on the *bottom* of other things, making sure to use the words *top* and *bottom* in sentences. For example: *The lamp is on top of the piano.*

WORD FAMILIES

-og, -op: pages 143-158

Continue to work on word families and, if necessary, review the word families from last month with the concentration cards from pages 115 and 121.

❏ Complete the worksheets.

❏ Make up a silly story about "The Frog and the Hog" with your child, challenging him or her to use as many -og words as possible. Do the same for the -op words with a story titled "Pop Likes To Hop."

❏ Write the -op words *hop, mop, top,* and *pop* on slips of paper and place them inside a small paper bag. Blow up the bag like a balloon. Ask your child to tell you the sound the bag will make when you pop it. Explain that *pop* ends with the letters -op. Pop the bag and ask your child to pick up the pieces of paper and read the -op words written on them.

Review Beginning Sounds
b, c, q, and v

Say each picture name. Color the pictures that begin with the sound of—

b = c = q = v =

You have made a patchwork quilt .

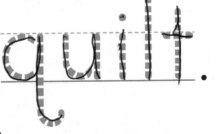

Review Beginning Sounds
p, w, y, z

Say the sound of the letter in each box and then the picture names. Draw lines from each letter to the pictures with the same beginning sound.

*Reviewing initial consonants **p, w, y, z***

Review Beginning Sounds
d, n, r, and s

Say the letter sound and then the picture name. Color the ☺ if the picture begins with that letter sound. Color the ☹ if it does not.

d

n

r

s

n

r

*Reviewing initial consonants **d, n, r, s***

133

Endings: d, g

The words in each box have the same ending sound.

 be**d**   sa**d**

 fla**g**   pi**g**

 Name the first picture in the row. Color the other pictures in the row that end with the same sound.

      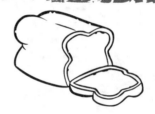   

Name each picture.
Write **d** or **g** to finish each word. Say the word.

do___   bir___   ta___

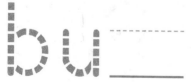 bu___   hea___   ru___

*Recognizing the sounds of **d** and **g** at the end of words*

Endings: n, t

The words in each box have the same ending sound.

 hen fan

 boat  net

 Name each picture. Write n or t to finish each word. Say the word.

ten   sun   pot

hat   pen   jet

Color the pictures that end with the letter in each box.

n

t

*Recognizing the sounds of **n** and **t** at the end of words*

Endings: p, x

The words in each box have the same ending sound.

map   soap

o<u>x</u>   6 si<u>x</u>

Name the first picture in the row. Color the other pictures in the row that end with the same sound.

Name each picture. Write **p** or **x** to finish each word. Say the word.

to __   mi __   ca __

6   ba __   cu __

si __   ba __   cu __

*Recognizing the sounds of **p** and **x** at the end of words*

Endings: b, m

The words in each box have the same ending sound.

ca**b**

bi**b**

 Name each picture. Write b or m to finish each word. Say the word.

tu**b**   ha**m**   dru**m**

 Circle 3 pictures with names that end with b.
 Color 3 pictures with names that end with m.

Recognizing the sounds of b and m at the end of words

137

Beginning Blends bl and cl

 **blanket**    **blouse**    **clown**    **clam**

 Look at the picture clues. Match each picture name to a word in the box. Then write each beginning sound to finish the puzzle.

black✓   block✓   blue✓   clip✓   clock✓   cloud✓

Across

1.

2.

3.

Down

1.

3.

4.

				1. C		I	P
			2.		O	C	K
					C		
3. b		A	4.		K		
U			O				
E			U				
			D				

*Recognizing initial consonant blends **bl** and **cl***

Beginning Blends fl and gl

flower   **flute**   **glove**   **glass**

 Say each picture name.
Write **fl** or **gl** to finish each word.

Gl ue   fl oor

fl ag   Gl obe

 Find the above words in the puzzle.
Circle each word.

F	L	A	G	R	X	G
L	B	I	L	Q	V	L
O	H	E	O	P	U	U
O	Z	F	B	Y	T	E
R	C	J	E	W	S	Y

*Recognizing initial consonant blends **fl** and **gl***

139

Beginning Blends pl and sl

plow   plug   sled   sleeve

 Help the 🛻 get back to the 🏠 .
Follow the path of pictures that begin with **pl**.

 Write **sl** at the beginning of each word to
answer the riddle.

You do this on an icy street.

You _____ ip and _____ ide.

*Recognizing initial consonant blends **pl** and **sl***

Hop to Short o

The word p**o**t has the short **o** sound.

Say each picture name.
Color the space green if you hear the short **o** sound.

Short o

Write o to finish each word. Trace the word. Draw a line to match each word with its picture.

m**o**p

t_p

l_ck

s_ck

f_x

t_g

Recognizing and writing words with the short sound of o

Words with og

The word **fr<u>og</u>** ends with the sounds for the letters **og**.

fr<u>og</u>

 Say each picture name. Read the word below it. Circle **og** in each word.

hog   **log**   **jog**

 Say the words. Trace the letters **og**. Say the sound at the end of each word.

frog   **log**

More Words with og

Say the words in each row. Circle the pictures with names that end with the same sound.

hog **log** **jog** **hen**

frog **fruit** **log** **hog**

jog **frog** **jet** **hog**

log **hog** **frog** **leg**

Recognizing words with -og

Rhyme Time

 and  have the same ending sounds.

 and  rhyme.

hog   **frog**

 Read the picture names aloud. Trace the first letter in each rhyming word.

 **_og**    **hog**

  Read the rhyming words. Trace over the beginning letters. Circle the frog on a log.

frog on a **log**

Match Them Up!

 Read the rhyming words. Color the pictures.

 **hog**    **log**    **frog**    **jog**

  Say each word. Trace the beginning letter. Draw a line to the matching picture.

jog

frog

log

hog

Recognizing words with -og

Play concentration!

log	**log**
hog	**hog**
frog	**frog**
jog	**jog**

Parents: Play concentration with two players. First cut apart the cards and place facedown. The first player turns over two cards and reads each word aloud. If they match, the player wins the pair. If not, the cards are turned face down and it's the second player's turn. The player with the most word pairs wins.

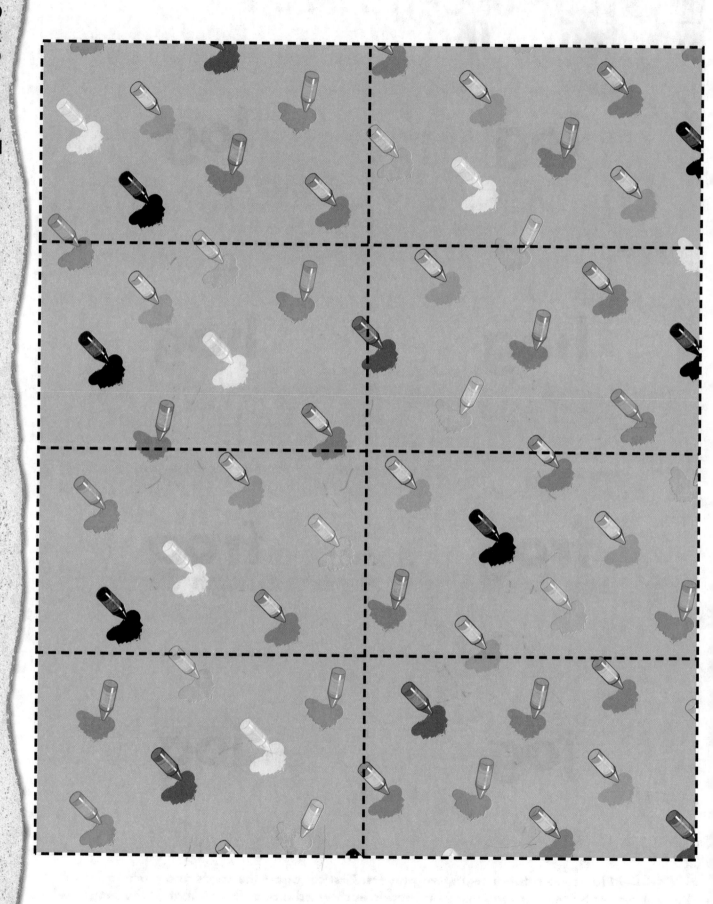

Recognizing words with **-og**

Words with op

T<u>op</u>  ends with the sound for the letters **op**.

t<u>op</u>

 Say each picture name. Read the word below it. Circle op in each word.

m(**op**)   **h**(**op**)   **t**(**op**)

 Say the words. Trace the letters op. Say the sounds at the end of each word.

s t o p   m o p

Recognizing words with -op

More Words with op

 Say the words in each row. Circle the pictures with names that end with the same sound.

mop   top   hop   men

stop   mop   step   top

top   tan   mop   stop

hop   top   hat   mop

Recognizing words with -op

Rhyme Time

 and have the same ending sound.

 and rhyme.

 **m<u>op</u>**    **t<u>op</u>**

 Read the picture names aloud. Trace the first letter in each rhyming word.

 hop    pop

  Read the rhyming words. Trace over the beginning letters. Circle the mop shop.

 mop

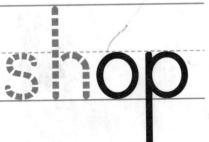 shop

*Recognizing words with **-op***

Match Them Up!

Read the rhyming words. Color the pictures.

top   **mop**   **pop**   **hop**

**Say each word. Trace the beginning letter.
Draw a line to the matching picture.**

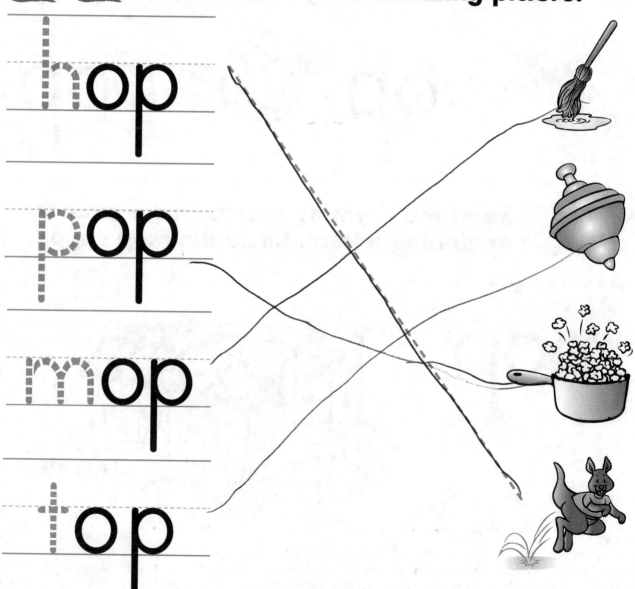

hop

pop

mop

top

*Recognizing words with **-op***

Play concentration!

shop	**shop**
top	**top**
stop	**stop**
pop	**pop**

Parents: Play concentration with two players. First cut apart the cards and place facedown. The first player turns over two cards and reads each word aloud. If they match, the player wins the pair. If not, the cards are turned face down and it's the second player's turn. The player with the most word pairs wins.

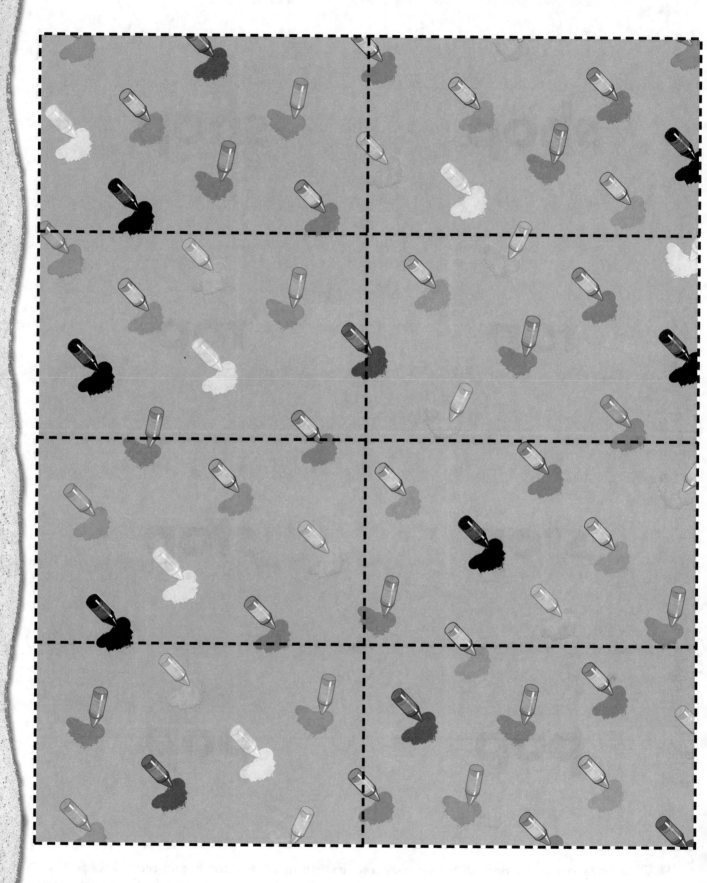

Recognizing words with **-op**

Parents: Remove pages 155-158 from this book. See directions for making mini storybooks on the inside of the front cover.

Top Hog

Flop goes Top Hog
on the log!
Hop, hop, hop,
goes the frog!

Top Hog, Top Hog,
jog, jog, Jog!

Look out, Top Hog!
A log! A log!

Chop, chop, Top Hog.
Chop that log!

Frog goes free!
Hop, hop, hop!

Top Hog, Top Hog,
mop, mop, mop!

Look out, Top Hog!
A frog! A frog! A frog!

Practice Test

Name each picture. Fill in the circle next to the letters for the ending sound.

● d
○ g
○ t

○ t
◐ n
● p

○ g
○ x
◐ t

○ n
◐ x
○ p

◐ g
○ d
○ t

● t
○ d
◐ p

○ x
◐ g
○ d

○ b
○ d
◐ m

○ n
○ t
● b

○ t
● d
◐ g

◐ t
○ d
○ n

○ x
○ t
◐ m

Practice Test

**Say the picture name.
Fill in the circle next to the correct word.**

10
- ○ tan
- ● ten
- ○ tin

- ○ fat
- ○ fig
- ● fox

6
- ○ sad
- ○ sled
- ● six

- ● fan
- ○ fed
- ○ fin

- ○ pan
- ○ pen
- ● pin

- ○ bat
- ○ beg
- ● box

- ○ leg
- ○ lid
- ● log

- ● hat
- ○ hid
- ○ hot

- ○ pat
- ○ peg
- ● pig

- ○ bat
- ○ big
- ○ boy

- ○ wag
- ○ web
- ○ win

- ○ bad
- ● bed
- ○ bib

*Recognizing words with short **a**, **e**, **i**, and **o***

Month 6 Checklist

Hands-on activities to help your child in school!

CONSONANTS

Ending Sounds: pages 163–164, 166–167

This month, your child will explore the ending sounds of *s, r, k, ll* and *ss.*

❏ Complete the worksheets.

❏ Play "What's In the Jar?" Write *r, k, ll,* and *ss* on a sheet of paper. Then write words that end with *r, k, ll,* or *ss* on slips of paper and put them in an empty jar. Have your child fish out a word from the jar. Then ask, "Does it end with ___?" Finish the sentence with one of the letters or letter pairs on the sheet. When your child answers correctly, have him or her read the word aloud. Try these words: *car, far, peek, week, ball, wall, pass, toss.*

❏ Have your child lie on a rug or blanket. Explain that the word *roll* ends with two *l*'s. Tell your child to listen carefully as you say some words. If a word ends with the *ll* sound, he or she should roll over. Use this list of words: *hand, hall, five, fun, fall, dog, doll, call, tent, tell.* You can play a similar game with a ball and the word *toss.* Have your child toss the ball when he or she hears a word that ends with the *ss* sound. Use these words: *pet, pass, mom, moss, green, grass, mess.*

BLENDS & DIGRAPHS

ck, ng, nt, nd, br, cr, dr, fr, gr, pr, tr: pages 165, 168–172, 191

The following activities will help your child recognize the sounds that *ck, ng, nt,* and *nd* make at the end of words and *br, cr, dr, fr, gr, pr,* and *tr* make at the beginning of words.

❏ Complete the worksheets.

❏ Hand your child a bell and point out that the word *ring* ends with the letters *ng.* Ask your child to listen carefully as you say some words. When you say a word that ends with *ng,* have your child ring the bell. Use these words: *short, long, bun, bang, hang, hippo, song, sun, sing, win, wing.* Vary the game by using other blends at the end of words:

- Have your child pretend to put on a *sock* when you a say word that ends in *ck.* Use these words: *back, base, click, chain, sack, sun, sick, tick.*
- Have your child raise a *hand* when you say a word that ends in *nd.* Use the following words: *hat, hand, box, band, wig, wind, supper, sand.*
- Finally, have your child *point* to the *front* of the room when you say a word that ends in *nt.* Use these words: *top, tent, hunt, ham, sent, sand, tuck, want.*

❏ Write the word *green* on an index card and point out that it begins with the letters *gr.* Challenge your child to go around your home and find things that are green. When he or she does, have your child hold up the card and say "*green.*"

VOWELS

Short *u:* pages 173–174, 192

In Month 6, your child also will practice the short sound of the vowel *u* (as in *bug*).

❑ Make "Short *u* Bugs." Write these words on a large sheet of paper: *hug, pot, cup, can, top, tug.* Tell your child that some of the words have the short *u* sound, as in the word *bug*. Have your child draw a bug above each word with the short *u* sound.

❑ Read a children's book or magazine with your child. Challenge him or her to find words with the letter *u* in them. Pronounce the word for your child and ask if he or she hears the short vowel sound of the letter *u*.

WORD FAMILIES

-*ub*, -*ug:* pages 175–190

Rounding out this month, your child will use the short *u* sound in words that end with -*ub* and -*ug*.

❑ Play a rhyming game. Say the following sentences and challenge your child to come up with a rhyming ending.

● "I saw a cute bug so I gave him a _____."

● "The dirty cub took a bath in a _____."

● "The tired old bug took a nap on a _____."

❑ Provide your child with some magazines and help him or her find words that end in -*ub*. Have your child use safety scissors to cut out the words. Then ask him or her to draw a bath tub and glue the -*ub* words in the tub.

❑ Write *ug* on an index card. Then write the letters *b, t, r,* and *m* on cards of their own. Put all the cards face down except for the *ug* card. Ask your child to turn over a card and put it in front of the *ug* card. Then have him or her say the word that it forms.

162

Review Ending Sounds
d, g, n, t

 Say each picture name.
Circle the letter that shows its ending sound.

 Color the pictures that end with the sound of g.

*Reviewing the sounds of **d, g, n,** and **t** at the end of words*

Review Ending Sounds p, x, b, m

 Say the sound of each letter.
Circle the pictures that end with that sound.

p

x

b

m

 Circle 4 pictures with names that end with the sound of **p**.

*Reviewing the sounds of **p**, **x**, **b**, and **m** at the end of words*

Review Beginning Sounds
bl, cl, fl, gl, pl, sl

Say the first word. Then write bl, cl, fl, gl, pl, or sl to finish the other words. Say them.

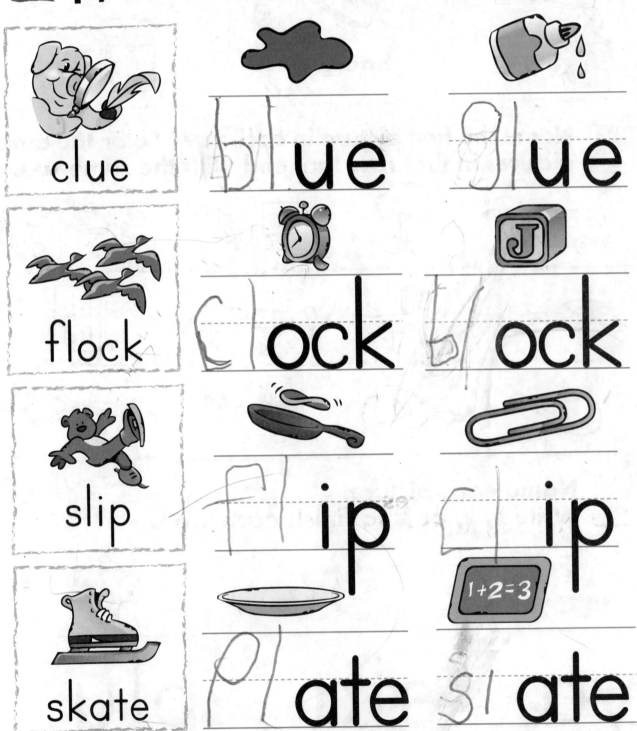

clue

blue   glue

flock

clock   block

slip

flip   slip

skate

plate   slate

Reviewing initial consonant blends bl, cl, fl, gl, pl, and sl

Ending Sounds: s, r, k

The words in each box have the same ending sound.

 Name the first picture in each row. Color the other pictures in that row that end with the same sound.

 Name each picture.
Write s, r, or k to finish each word.

ya___ sta___ plu___

166

*Recognizing the sounds of **s**, **r**, and **k** at the end of words*

Endings: ll, ss

The words in each box have the same ending sound.

 be**ll**  do**ll**

 dre**ss** gra**ss**

 Name each picture.
Write ll or ss to finish each word. Say the word.

gla___ g___ ba___ ___ gra___ g___

hi___ ki___ do___

 Draw a line from the sentence to the picture
it tells about.

 Pass the ball.

The glass is full.

Ending Digraph ck

These words have the same ending sound.

clock

duck

 Say each picture name. Write ck on the lines only if you hear the same ending sound as in  and .

 tru_____

 fi_____

be_____

bla_____

 Say each picture name. Draw a line from the to the pictures with the same ending sound.

*Recognizing the sound of **ck** at the end of words*

Ending Sounds: ng, nt, nd

The words in each box end with the same sound.

wing

ring

a_nt_

te_nt_

ha_nd_

wa_nd_

 Name each picture. Write ng, nt, or nd to finish each word. Say the word.

pla_nt_   ba_n_d   ki_n_g

 Say each picture name. If it ends in ng, nt, or nd, color as follows:

nd   nt   ng

---

*Recognizing the sounds of **ng**, **nt**, and **nd** at the end of words*

Beginning Sounds br, cr

The words in each box begin with the same sound.

brush

braid

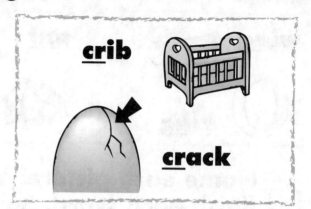

crib

crack

 Look at each picture. Find its name in the orange box. Then write the beginning sounds to finish the puzzle.

brown   crab

brick   broom

crown   crow

Across

2.

5.

Down

1.

2.

3.

4.

						¹
²		I	³	K		
				⁴		O
O			A			W
O		⁵			O	W	N
M					W		

*Recognizing initial consonant blends **br** and **cr***

Beginning Sounds dr, fr, gr

The words in each box begin with the same sound.

drum

drip

frog

frost

grapes

grass

Name each picture. Write **dr**, **fr**, or **gr** to finish each word.

ill   ess   uit

Say the names of the pictures in each box. Draw lines from the letters to the pictures with the same beginning sound.

dr

fr

*Recognizing initial consonant blends **dr**, **fr**, and **gr***

Beginning Sounds pr, tr

The words in each box begin with the same sound.

pretzel

prize

track

tree

 Look at the pictures. Read the words in the box.
Write pr or tr to finish each word.
Then tell a picture story.

tree
trunk
prince
pretty

 cat in a __tree__

 sad __prince__

 boy climbs up __trunk__

 __pretty__ cat!

*Recognizing initial consonant blends **pr** and **tr***

Fun With Short u

The word **cup** has the short **u** sound.

 Say each picture name.
Connect the pictures that have the short u sound.

START

Recognizing the short vowel sound of **u**

Short u

 Write **u** to finish each word. Trace the word. Read the word.

s u n

n t

r g

j g

 Find 2 other things in the picture that have the short **u** sound. Write the names for the pictures.

b

c

*Recognizing words with the short sound of **u***

Words with ub

The word **c<u>ub</u>**  ends with the sound for the letters **ub**.

cub

 Say each picture name. Read the word below it. Circle ub in each word.

t<u>ub</u>　　　　**sub**　　　　**rub**

 Say the words. Trace the letters ub. Say the sound at the end of each word.

cub　　　**sub**

Recognizing words with -ub

More Words with ub

Say the names of the pictures in each row. Circle the pictures with names that have the same ending sound.

tub

sub

cub

ten

club

clock

cub

tub

cub

club

cow

rub

sub

scrub

sun

tub

*Recognizing words with **-ub***

Rhyme Time

 and have the same ending sounds.
 and rhyme.

 **tub**

 **cub**

 Say the picture names. Read the rhyming words below them. Trace the first letter in each word.

sub

tub

 **Read the rhyming words. Trace the first letters in each word. Then circle the cub club.**

cub **club**

*Recognizing words with **-ub***

Match Them Up!

 Read the rhyming words. Then color the pictures.

club   sub   tub   cub

  Say each word. Then trace the beginning letters. Draw a line to each matching picture.

tub

club

sub

cub

*Recognizing words with **-ub***

Play concentration!

sub	sub
cub	cub
tub	tub
rub	rub

Parents: Play concentration with two players. First cut apart the cards and place face down. The first player turns over two cards and reads each word aloud. If they match, the player wins the pair. If not, the cards are turned face down and it's the second player's turn. The player with the most word pairs wins.

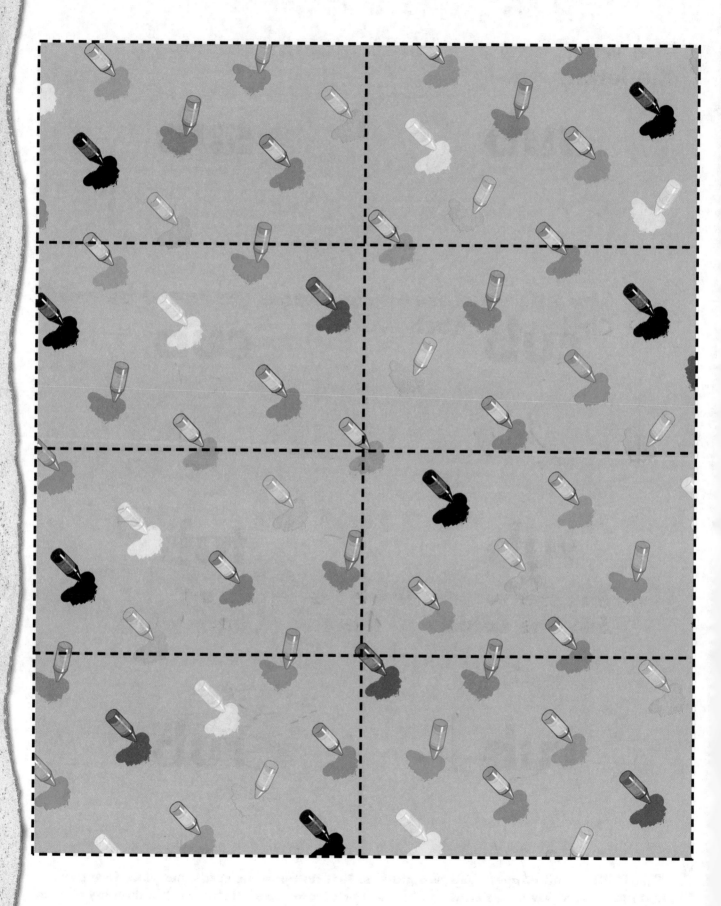

Recognizing words with -ub

Words with ug

The word **b<u>ug</u>**  ends with the sounds for the letters **ug.**

bug

 Say each picture name. Read the word below it. Circle **ug** in each word.

m(ug)   **rug**   **hug**

 Say the words. Trace the letters **ug.** Say the sounds at the end of each word.

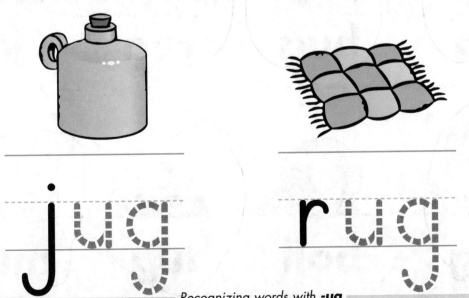

jug   rug

Recognizing words with -ug

More Words with ug

Say the names of the pictures in each row. Circle the pictures with names that have the same ending sound.

rug **bug** **jug** **rat**

hug **mug** **hen** **bug**

jug **bug** **rug** **jet**

bug **ball** **tug** **mug**

Recognizing words with -ug

Rhyme Time

 and have the same ending sounds.

 and  rhyme.

 **mug**

 **bug**

 Say the picture names. Read the rhyming words next to them. Trace the first letter in each word.

m**ug**

j**ug**

 Read the rhyming words.
Trace the first letters in each word.
Then circle the **snug bug.**

sn**ug**

b**ug**

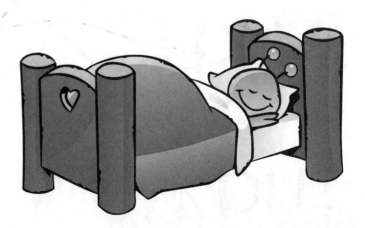

Match Them Up!

 **Read the rhyming words. Then color the pictures.**

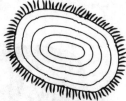 

mug **rug** **bug** **jug**

  Say each word. Then trace the beginning letter. Draw a line to each matching picture

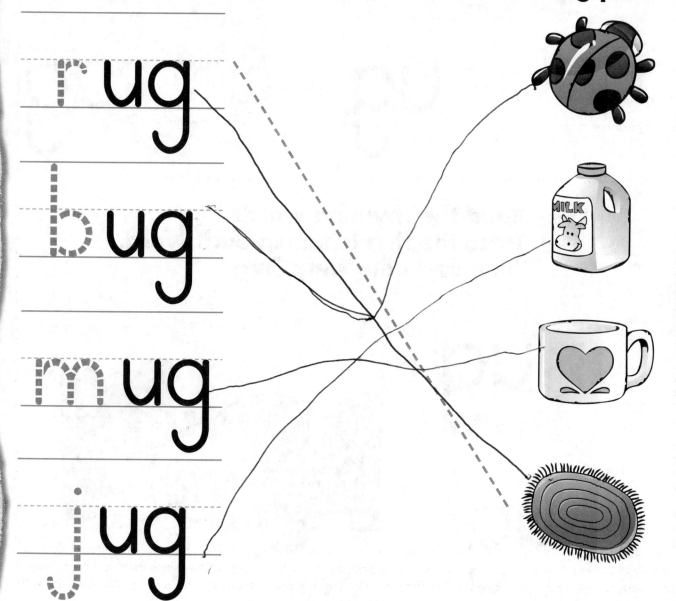

rug

bug

mug

jug

184 *Recognizing words with* **-ug**

Play concentration!

rug | **rug**

hug | **hug**

mug | **mug**

bug | **bug**

Parents: Play concentration with two players. First cut apart the cards and place face down. The first player turns over two cards and reads each word aloud. If they match, the player wins the pair. If not, the cards are turned face down and it's the second player's turn. The player with the most word pairs wins.

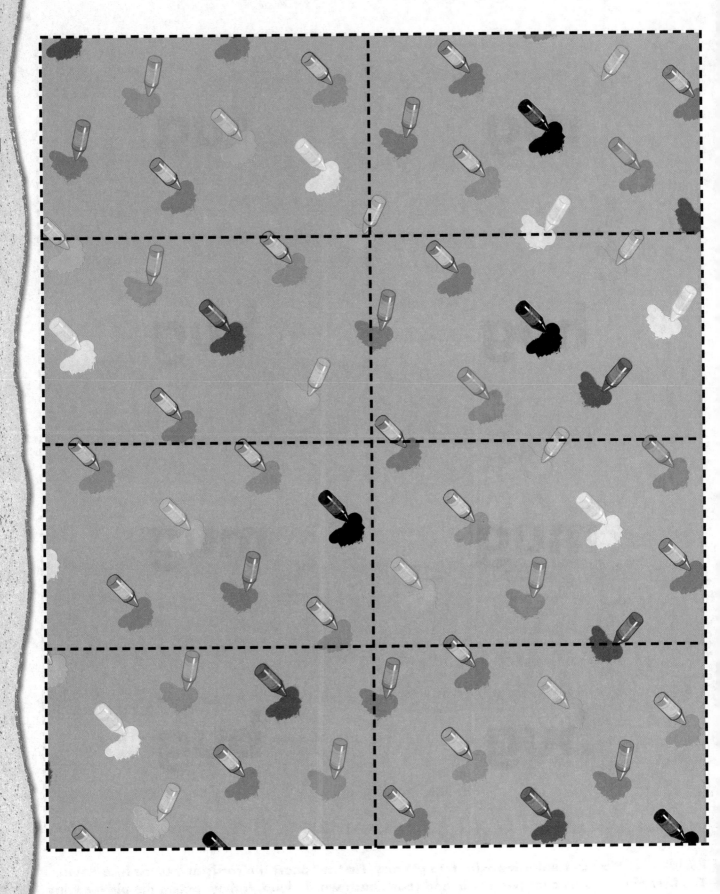

Recognizing words with **-ug**

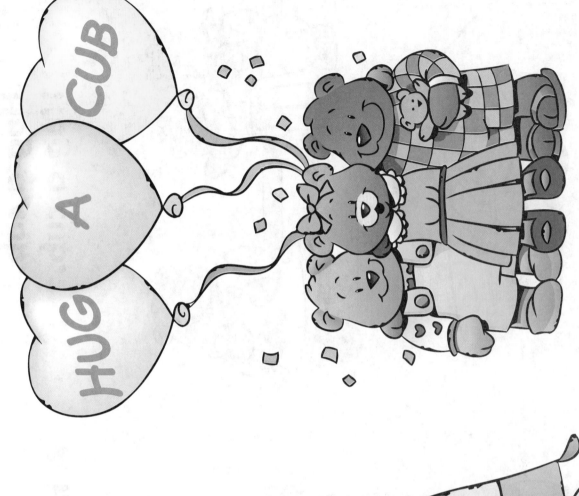

Hug! Hug!
Give a bug a hug at the Cub Club.

Hug a cub.
Hug a cub.

A bug! A bug!
A bug is in the Cub Club!

Hug a cub
at the Cub Club.

Hug a cub.
Hug a cub
at the Cub Club.

Cubs on a rug
at the Cub Club.

A mug for a cub
at the Cub Club.

Practice Test

Say the picture name.
Fill in the circle next to the correct word.

○ clap
○ drop
● tree

● dress
○ flag
○ slap

○ play
○ drip
● flag

○ plum
● clock
○ brim

○ truck
○ clip
● drum

● blue
○ grip
○ fly

○ prize
○ drive
● cloud

● broom
○ trip
○ glue

○ grill
○ floor
● crib

○ sleep
● train
○ dress

○ print
○ block
○ price

● clip
○ drip
○ flip

Recognizing initial consonant blends with -l and -r

Practice Test

 Say the picture name. Fill in the circle next to the correct word.

- ○ dip
- ○ dog
- ● duck

- ○ hat
- ○ hug
- ○ ham

- ○ bag
- ○ bug
- ○ big

- ○ pan
- ○ plum
- ○ pig

- ○ tap
- ○ tub
- ○ top

- ○ jug
- ○ jam
- ○ jog

- ○ cap
- ○ cup
- ○ clip

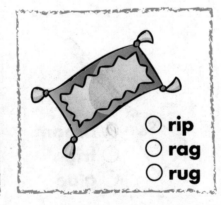
- ○ rip
- ○ rag
- ○ rug

- ○ bell
- ○ bug
- ○ bag

- ○ jug
- ○ jet
- ○ jar

- ○ bad
- ○ bat
- ○ bus

- ○ bib
- ○ bug
- ○ bat

Recognizing words with short vowel sounds

Month 7 Checklist

Hands-on activities to help your child in school!

BLENDS & DIGRAPHS

Review endings *ck, ng, nt, nd:* pages 195, 224
Review blends with *r:* pages 196–197
Blends *sm, sp, sn, sw, st, str, spr:* pages 198–200, 222
Digraphs *ch, sh, th, wh:* pages 201–204, 223

Blends are letter combinations in which the sounds of each letter are still discernible. *Digraphs*, on the other hand, are letter combinations that make a unique sound. For example, in the word *shoe*, you do not hear the separate sounds of *s* or *h*, but an entirely new sound. Digraphs may appear at the beginning or end of a word (for example, <u>sh</u>oe and di<u>sh</u>). Use the activities below to work on both blends and digraphs.

❏ Complete the worksheets.
❏ Have your child sit at the kitchen table. Write the words *smell* and *sniff* on a piece of paper and help your child read them aloud. Point out the blends *sm* and *sn*. Ask your child to close his or her eyes as you hold out a piece of food. Tell him or her to say "*Sniff. Sniff. I smell a* _____." Then have your child open his or her eyes to see if the guess was right. Continue with other foods.
❏ Write the blends and digraphs *sw, st, str, spr, th,* and *ing* on individual cards. Place the cards facedown, except for *ing*. Ask your child to turn over a card and put it in front of *ing*. Then help him or her read the word that it forms.
❏ The next time you're driving, point out the word *stop* on a stop sign. Then play this game: every time your child sees a stop sign, he or she must say a word—other than *stop*—that begins with *st*.
❏ Take a bundle of drinking straws and spread them out on the kitchen table. Point out that the word *straw* begins with *str*. Use the straws to form the letters *str*. Then mix them up and let your child have a turn. Repeat this game until you've reviewed the other blends and digraphs. Challenge your child to say a word that uses each letter combination as it is presented.

WORD FAMILIES

-am, -ap: pages 205–220

Review any of the word families presented in previous months, as desired, as you continue with two new ones this month: -am and -ap.

❏ Complete the worksheets.

❏ Explain that the word *clap* ends with the letters -ap. Have your child say the word *clap* and clap his or her hands. Then say, "Listen. If I say a word that rhymes with *clap*, clap your hands." Say the words *map, moss, mom, toss, tap, train, trap, coin, cake, cap, fling, flap.*

❏ Make an "-am Yam." You will need a large yam, some small pieces of paper, tape, and some toothpicks. Tell your child that the word *yam* ends with the letters -am. Make a little flag with paper, a toothpick, and tape. Write the word *clam* on it. Have your child read the word aloud and stick the flag in the yam. Continue with the words *ham, am, ram, swam, and slam.* Throughout the week, challenge your child to read the flags in the "-am Yam."

❏ Have your child go on an "-am Hunt." Write a word that ends in -am on an index card and hide it in your home. Encourage your child to find the card by having him or her ask you this question: "<u>Am</u> I getting closer?" (Make sure your child stresses the word *am.*) Answer yes or no. When the -am card is found, have the child read it aloud. You can also play the game with words ending with -ap.

VOWELS

Short Vowel Review: page 221

Help your child practice listening for the short sounds of *a, e, i, o,* and *u* as often as possible.

❏ Complete the worksheets.

❏ Read aloud a children's book or magazine. Challenge your child to find words with short vowel sounds in them. Pronounce each word and ask, "Do you hear the short vowel sound at the beginning, middle, or end of the word?"

Review Ending Sounds
ck, ng, nt, nd

 Say each picture name. Circle the letters that show its ending sound.

(nt)   ck

(ng)   nd

nt   (ck)

(nd)   ng

(ck)   ng

nt   ck

(nt)   ng

(nd)   ng

ng   (ck)

nd   ng

nd   (ng)

(ck)   ng

nt   ck

ck   (ng)

nd   nt

(ck)   nt

 Color the pictures that end with the sound of ck.

*Reviewing the sounds of **ck, ng, nt,** and **nd** at the end of words*

Review Beginning Sounds
br, cr, dr, fr

Say each picture name. Write br, cr, dr, or fr to finish the word.

ab

idge

ip

ide

og

ib

ame

ill

ush

Reviewing the initial consonant blends br, cr, dr, and fr

Review Beginning Sounds
gr, pr, tr

**Help the troll find his trunk.
Name each picture on the path.
Circle the word for each picture.**

grass
tree

grapes
tray

prince
track

train
prize

truck
brick

brown
green

grill
print

---

*Reviewing the initial consonant blends **gr**, **pr**, and **tr***

Beginning Sounds sm, sp

The words in each box begin with the same sound.

smile

smoke

spoon

spill

 Look at the pictures. Read the words in the box. Write sm or sp to finish each word.

| smell | smile | spell | spoon |

smile

sm**ell**

sp**oon**

sp**ell**

 Read the word. Color the picture that matches the word.

small

spill

Recognizing the initial consonant blends sm and sp

Beginning Sounds sn, st, sw

The words in each box begin with the same sound.

<u>sn</u>ail

<u>sn</u>ake

<u>st</u>ool

<u>st</u>airs

<u>sw</u>im

<u>sw</u>ing

 Look at the pictures. Write the word from the box that matches each picture.

| stir | swan | stick | sniff | stamp | swim |

stick

swan

stir

sniff

stamp

swim

BLENDS & DIGRAPHS

Beginning Sounds str, spr

The words in each box begin with the same sound.

straw

stream

spring

spray

 **Say and trace each word.
Circle the matching picture.**

street

spring

 **Name each picture. Color the pictures
that begin with str.**

*Recognizing the initial consonant blends **str** and **spr***

Beginning and Ending ch

The words in this box begin with the same sound.

<u>ch</u>air   **<u>ch</u>eese**

The words in this box end with the same sound.

ben<u>ch</u>   **bran<u>ch</u>**

 Name each picture. Circle 🚦 if the name **begins** with **ch**. Circle 🚦 if the name **ends** with **ch**.

 Circle **3** things in the picture that begin with **ch**.

*Recognizing the consonant digraph **ch***

Beginning and Ending sh

The words in this box begin with the same sound.

shoe   **shell**

The words in this box end with the same sound.

bush   **dish**

Say each picture name. Draw lines from the 🐚 to the pictures with the same beginning sound.

Name the pictures. Write sh to finish each word.

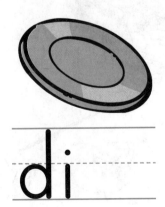

di _____

tra _____

*Recognizing the consonant digraph **sh***

Beginning and Ending th

The words in this box begin with the same sound.	The words in this box end with the same sound.

thumb **thirteen**	**moth** **tooth**

  Write th to finish each word. Draw a line to match each word with its picture.

_____ umb

_____ orn

ba _____

_____ roat

*Recognizing the consonant digraph **th*** — **203**

Beginning Sound wh

These words begin with the same sound.

 __wh__ale   __wh__eel

 Say each picture name. Color the space if the name has the same beginning sound as .

Question words begin with wh. Write wh to finish the question. Then answer it.

_____cat is your name?

Words with am

The word **clam**  ends with the sounds for the letters **am**.

clam

 Say each picture name. Read the word below it. Circle **am** in the word.

ham **ram** **jam**

 Say the words. Trace the letters **am**. Say the sounds at the end of each word.

 clam ham

More Words with am

 Say the names of the pictures in each row. Circle the pictures with names that have the same ending sounds.

 **ham**    **yam**    **hat**    **clam**

 **ram**    **ham**    **jam**    **ring**

 **clam**    **clock**    **ham**    **ram**

 **jam**    **jet**    **clam**    **yam**

206   *Recognizing words with* **-am**

Rhyme Time

 and have the same ending sounds.

 and rhyme.

 **ram**

 **clam**

 Say the picture names. Read the rhyming words next to them. Trace the first letter in each word.

 ram

 jam

  Trace the first letter in each word. Then circle the **ham** and **yam** in the picture.

ham

and

yam

Recognizing words with -am

207

Match Them Up!

**Read the rhyming words.
Then color the pictures.**

ham   **ram**   **jam**   **clam**

  Say the words and trace the beginning
letters. Match each word to a picture.

clam

ram

ham

jam

Recognizing words with -am

Play concentration!

ram	ram
yam	**yam**
clam	clam
jam	jam

Parents: Play concentration with two players. First cut apart the cards and place face down. The first player turns over two cards and reads each word aloud. If they match, the player wins the pair. If not, the cards are turned face down and it's the second player's turn. The player with the most word pairs wins.

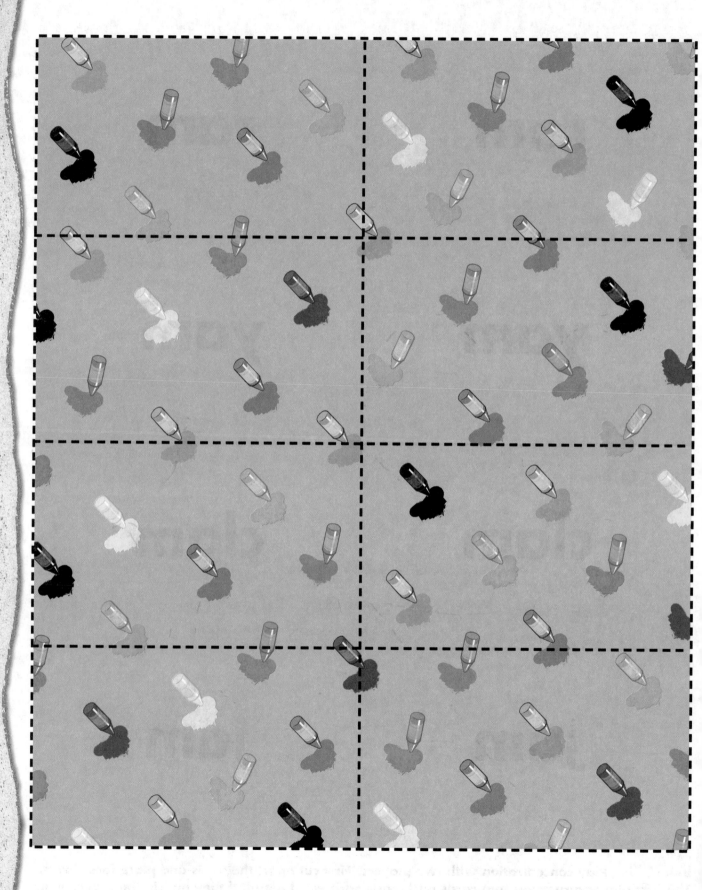

Recognizing words with -am

Words with ap

The word **map** ends with the sounds for the letters **ap**.

m<u>ap</u>

 Say each picture name. Read the word below it. Circle **ap** in the word.

cap **lap** **nap**

 Say the words. Trace the letters **ap**. Say the sounds at the end of each word.

Recognizing words with -ap

More Words with ap

Say the names of the pictures in each row. Circle the pictures with names that have the same ending sounds.

cap

map

cake

lap

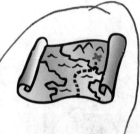

map

men

cap

nap

clap

cap

clock

lap

tap

map

cap

tent

Recognizing words with -ap

Rhyme Time

 and have the same ending sounds.

 and rhyme.

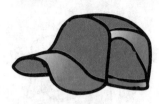 **cap**

 **nap**

 Say the picture names. Read the rhyming words next to them. Trace the first letter in each word.

 c a p

 m a p

 Trace the beginning letters in the words below. Then circle **tap** and **clap** in the picture.

 t a p    c l a p

WORD FAMILIES

Match Them Up!

 Read the rhyming words.
Then color the pictures.

 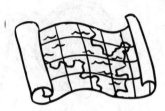  

nap　　　**map**　　　**cap**　　　**lap**

  Say each word. Then trace the beginning letter. Draw a line to match each word to a picture.

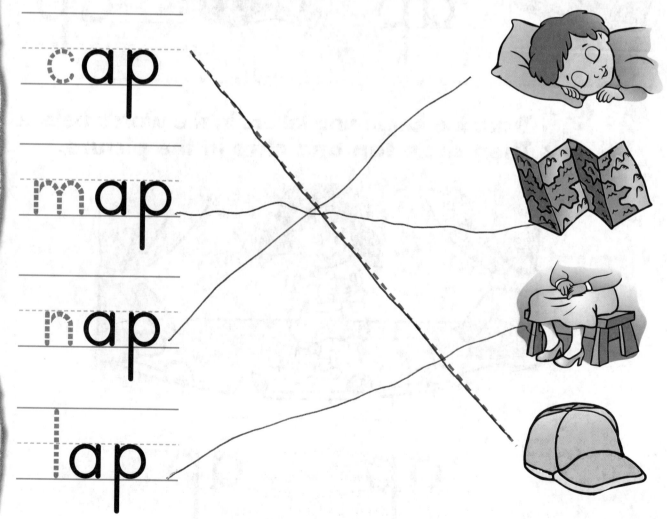

cap

map

nap

lap

　　Recognizing words with -ap

Play concentration!

nap	**nap**
clap	**clap**
tap	**tap**
snap	**snap**

Parents: Play concentration with two players. First cut apart the cards and place facedown. The first player turns over two cards and reads each word aloud. If they match, the player wins the pair. If not, the cards are turned face down and it's the second player's turn. The player with the most word pairs wins.

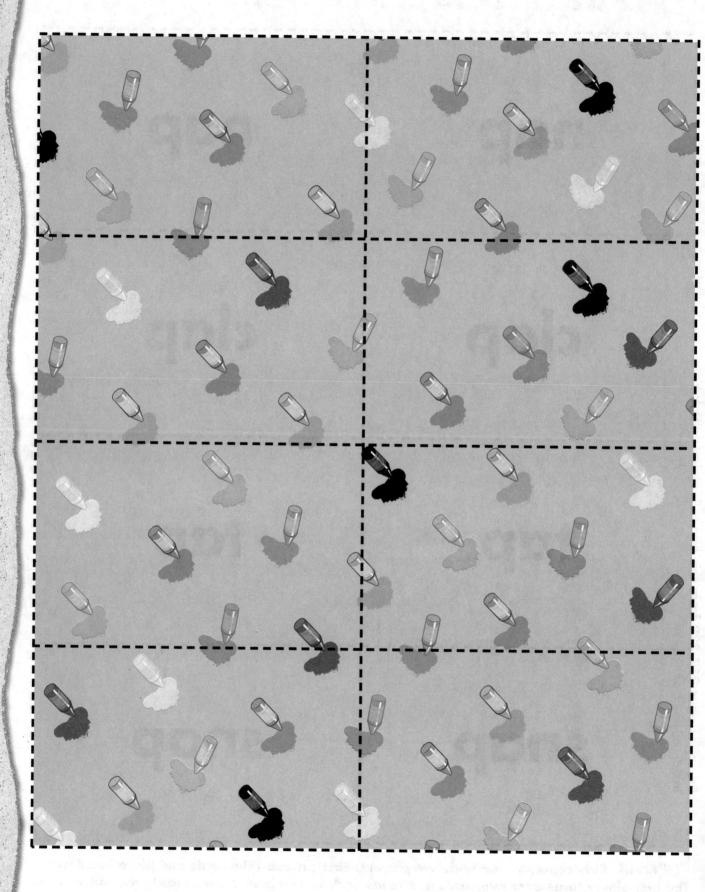

Recognizing words with -ap

Parents: Remove pages 217-220 from this book. See directions for making mini storybooks on the inside of the front cover.

SNAP THE CLAM

"Snap! Snap!
Mmmm! A clam!
Delicious!"

"Snap! Snap!"

"A clam! A clam!"

"A clam! A clam!"

"Snap! Snap!"

"Snap! Snap!"

"A clam! A clam!"

Short Vowel Review

 Name each picture.
Write the letter to finish each word.

p i g

c a t

p e n

b u g

m o p

f i s h

c l o c k

n e t

b u s

*Completing words with the short sounds of **a, e, i, o,** and **u***

Practice Test

Say the picture name. Fill in the circle next to the correct word.

- ● smile
- ○ snack
- ○ swim

- ● spoon
- ○ stand
- ○ strap

- ○ smell
- ○ spot
- ● star

- ● snail
- ○ snow
- ○ stone

- ○ small
- ○ snip
- ● swim

- ○ smoke
- ● spin
- ● straw

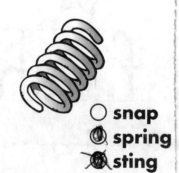
- ○ snap
- ● spring
- ● sting

- ● snake
- ○ spot
- ○ stair

- ● stamp
- ○ swamp
- ○ swim

- ○ store
- ○ sniff
- ● spray

- ○ spend
- ○ spring
- ● swing

- ○ small
- ○ sniff
- ● string

*Recognizing blends with **s***

Practice Test

Say the picture name.
Fill in the circle next to the correct word.

- ● cheese
- ○ shell
- ○ thick

- ○ check
- ○ shed
- ◉ whale

- ○ chip
- ○ shop
- ◉ thumb

- ◉ check
- ⊗ shack
- ○ thin

- ⊗ chick
- ◉ shark
- ○ what

- ○ chin
- ○ shell
- ◉ wheel

- ○ bath
- ◉ bench
- ○ bush

- ○ fast
- ◉ fish
- ○ five

- ○ bat
- ◉ bath
- ○ beach

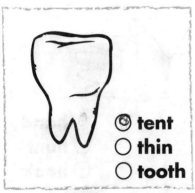

- ◉ tent
- ○ thin
- ○ tooth

- ◉ brush
- ○ buck
- ○ show

- ○ wand
- ◉ watch
- ○ wish

*Recognizing the consonant digraphs **ch**, **sh**, **th**, and **wh***

Practice Test

Say the picture name. Fill in the circle next to the correct word.

- ○ can
- ○ cat
- ● cup

- ● box
- ○ bus
- ○ bat

- ○ jar
- ● jam
- ○ jog

- ○ rock
- ○ run
- ● ring

- ● sock
- ○ song
- ○ sun

- ○ tot
- ● tent
- ○ thin

- ● peach
- ○ pass
- ○ plan

- ○ ding
- ● dish
- ○ dock

- ○ dam
- ● duck
- ○ dash

- ○ moth
- ○ much
- ○ mash

- ○ stand
- ● stick
- ○ stir

- ● hand
- ○ hunt
- ○ hook

Recognizing consonants, blends, and digraphs at the end of words

Month 8 Checklist

BLENDS & DIGRAPHS

Blends with *l* and *r*: pages 227-228; 255
Blends *sm, sn, sp, st, sw, spr, str*: pages 229-230; 255
Digraphs *ch, sh, th, wh*: pages 231, 255

Work on blends and digraphs continues this month with the following activities:

❏ Complete the worksheets.

❏ As you look through a children's book, ask your child to find words that begin with one of the blends or digraphs listed above. For example, have him or her look for words beginning with *sh* and help the child sound them out. After a few words, switch to a different beginning sound.

❏ Play "String Thing." Hand one end of a ball of string to your child as you point out that the word *string* begins with the letters *str*. Then choose another blend, such as *cl*, and say, "Now walk with the string until you find something that begins with *cl*." (clip, closet, clippers, etc.) Hold one end of the string and let it unwind as your child searches. Repeat this for words beginning and ending with other blends and digraphs.

CONSONANTS

Words ending with *d, g, n, t, x, p, b, m, ll, ss*: pages 232-233
Words beginning with soft *c*, soft *g*: pages 234-235

In addition to more work with ending sounds, this month's activities focus on beginning soft *c*, as in the word *cent*, and soft *g*, as in the word *gym*.

❏ Complete the worksheets.

❏ Invite your child to watch as you make a "Soft C Shopping List." Write the following words on a slip of paper: *cereal, cider, celery, cinnamon*. Read each word aloud, pointing out the soft *c* sound. On your next trip to the supermarket, take along the Soft C Shopping List and help your child find the items (even if you don't purchase them).

❏ Help your child distinguish between the sound of hard *g*, as in *goal*, and soft *g*, as in *gel*. Ask your child to pretend he or she is a famous gymnast by doing some jumping jacks. Point out that *gymnast* starts with the soft *g* sound. Then say, "Listen carefully as I say some words. If a word begins with the soft *g* sound, do a jumping jack. If it's the hard *g* sound, sit down." Use this wordlist: *gym, goat, game, germ, giraffe, gift, gerbil, gate, giant, gab, gel, gentle.*

VOWELS

Short Vowels: pages 236-237; 256
Long *a*: pages 238-252, 256
In addition to reviewing short vowels, this month your child will learn about the long *a* sound that is spelled with the letters *ai* (as in *rain*), *ay* (as in *ray*), and *a_e* (as in *cave*).

❏ Complete the worksheets.

❏ Write *ail* on one index card and the letters *m, t, r, p, f, n, sn,* and *tr* on cards of their own. Place the cards facedown, except for the *ail* card. Ask your child to turn over a card, put it in front of *ail* and say the word that it forms. Repeat this activity with an *ay* card and the letters *b, d, h, m, p, r, s, w, cl, pl,* and *tr*.

❏ Help your child understand how adding the letter *e* to the end of a word often creates a long vowel sound. Write the word *tap* on a piece of paper and ask your child to say the word. Then write an *e* at the end of the word. Challenge him or her to read the new word aloud (*tape*). Continue this activity with the words *cap, fat, rat, Sam, can, man,* and *plan*.

WORD PARTS

Plurals ending with *-s* and *-es*: pages 253-254
At the end of Month 8, your child will be shown how words can become plural by adding *-s* or *-es*.

❏ Complete the worksheets.

❏ Give your child two crayons and hold up one crayon. Say, "I have one crayon." Have your child complete the sentence, "I have two _____." Walk around your home picking up an object and then handing your child two of them. Say the sentence, "I have one ____," and your child will respond with his or her sentence, "I have two ____ ," with the correct plural ending.

❏ Read aloud a picture book. When you come to plural words that end in *-s* or *-es*, point them out. If there is an illustration of the plural word, have your child point to it.

Review Blends with l

Say the letter sounds and picture names in each box. Draw a line between each picture and its beginning sound.

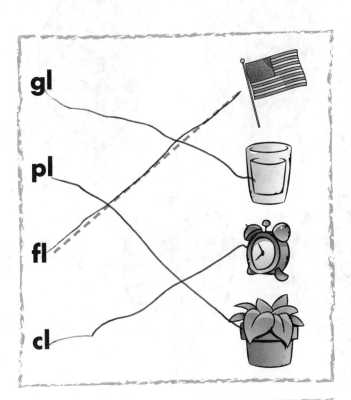

gl

pl

fl

cl

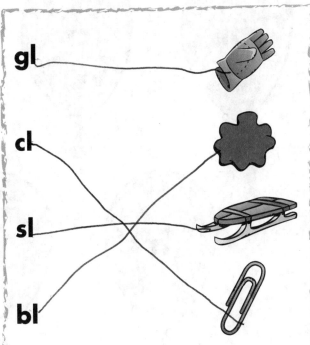

gl

cl

sl

bl

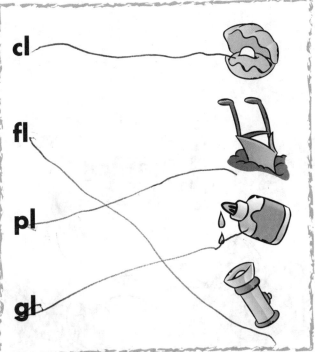

cl

fl

pl

gl

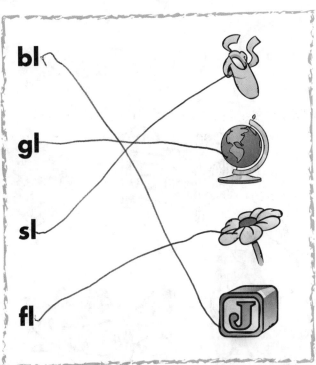

bl

gl

sl

fl

Reviewing initial blends with -l

227

Review Blends with r

 Say each picture name. Draw a string from each picture to the balloon with the correct beginning sound.

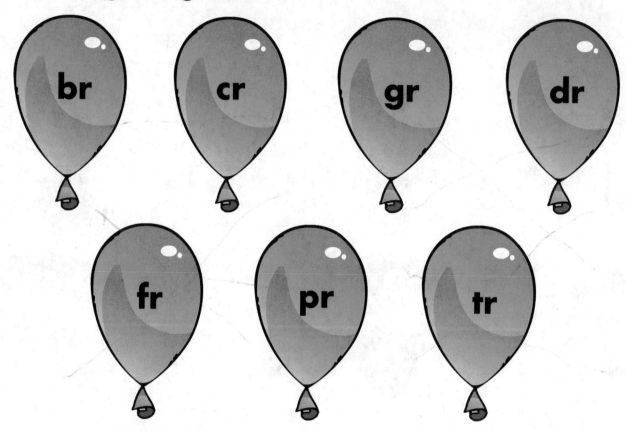

br cr gr dr

fr pr tr

Reviewing initial blends with -r

Review Beginning Blends
sm, sn, sp, st, sw

 Say each picture name. Circle the letters that show its beginning sounds.

sp (sw)

(sm) sp

sn (st)

sn (sp)

(sp) st

st (sw)

sw (sm)

(sn) sw

(sn) sp

sn (sw)

sp (st)

sm (sn)

 Write the letters that are missing from the sign. Color the sign red.

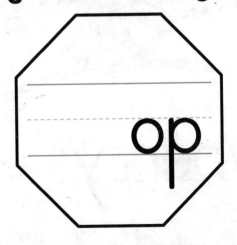

op

Review Beginning Blends spr, str

Help the kitten follow the string. Say each picture name. Write **str** or **spr** to finish each word.

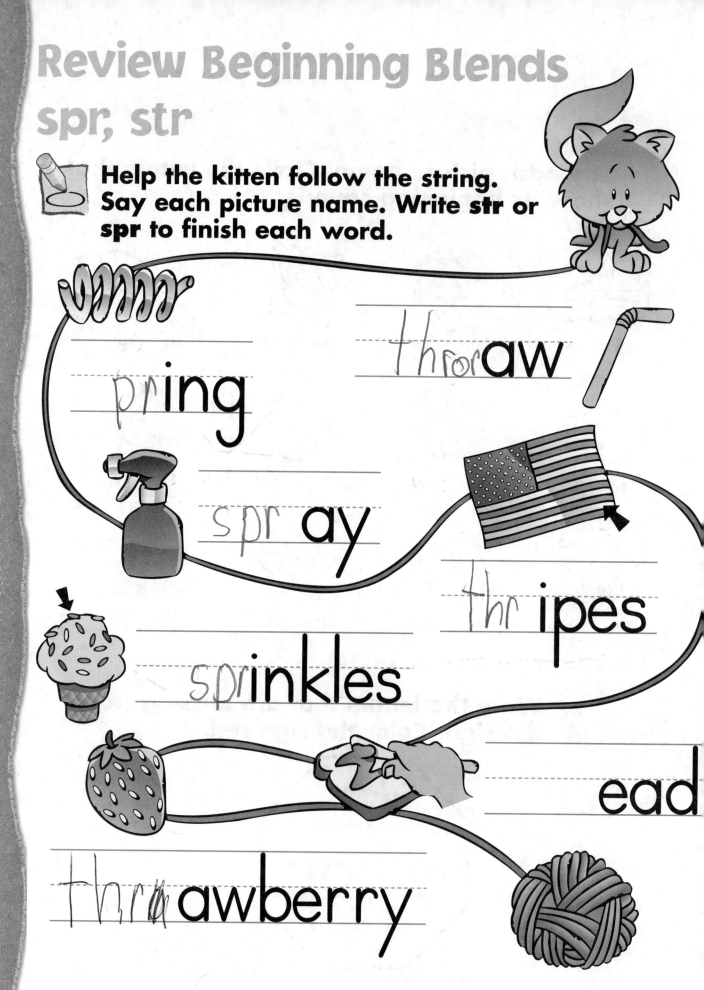

pr**ing**

thro**aw**

spr**ay**

thr**ipes**

spr**inkles**

ead

thr**awberry**

Reviewing the blends str and spr

Review Sounds ch, sh, th, wh

 What did the whale eat? Say each picture name. If it starts with the sound of —

ch= sh=

th= wh=

 **Say each picture name.
Write sh, ch, or th to finish each word.**

too   fi_h_t   bran th

Reviewing the digraphs ch, sh, th, and wh

Review Endings d, g, n, t, x

**Write d, g, n, t, or x to finish each word.
Find the pictures that show the words.
Color them. Then say the words.**

fro

fo

ne

she

wago

*Reviewing the sounds of **d, g, n, t,** and **x** at the end of words*

Review Endings b, m, p, ll, ss

 Say each picture name. Draw a line from the picture to another picture that ends with the same sound. Write the letter that stands for that sound.

_____

_____

_____

_____

_____

 Say each picture name. Listen for the ending sound. Write ll or ss to finish each word.

ba_____   we_____   gla_____

Beginning Soft c

Sometimes the letter **c** has the **s** sound. It stands for the sound at the beginning of .

 **Name each picture. Write c under the ones that start like .**

_____

c

_____

_____

_____

_____

_____

_____

_____

_____

Recognizing the soft sound of initial consonant c

Beginning Soft g

Sometimes the letter g
has the j sound. It stands for
the sound at the beginning of .

 Name each picture.
Write g under the ones that start like .

_____

_ _ _ _ _ _ _ _ _ _ _ _

_ _ _ _ _ _ _ _ _ _ _ _

_____

_ _ _ _ _ _ _ _ _ _ _ _

_ _ _ _ _ _ _ _ _ _ _ _

_____

_ _ _ _ _ _ _ _ _ _ _ _

_ _ _ _ _ _ _ _ _ _ _ _

Recognizing the soft sound of initial consonant **g**

Fred Finds His Home

Help Fred Fish go home. Name each picture Fred finds. Fill in the missing letter. Write a, e, i, o, or u. Keep going until you get Fred home!

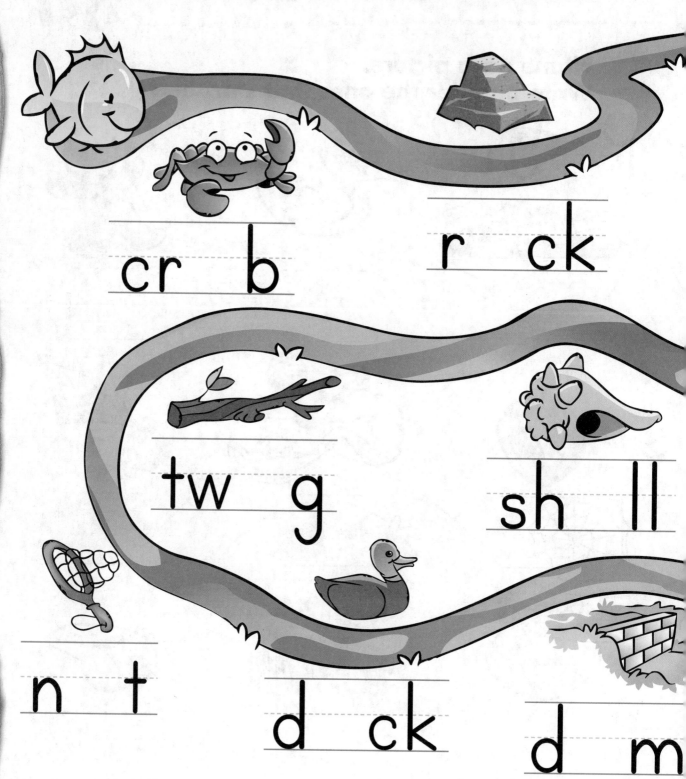

cr_b

r_ck

tw_g

sh_ll

n_t

d_ck

d_m

Reviewing short vowels: word maze

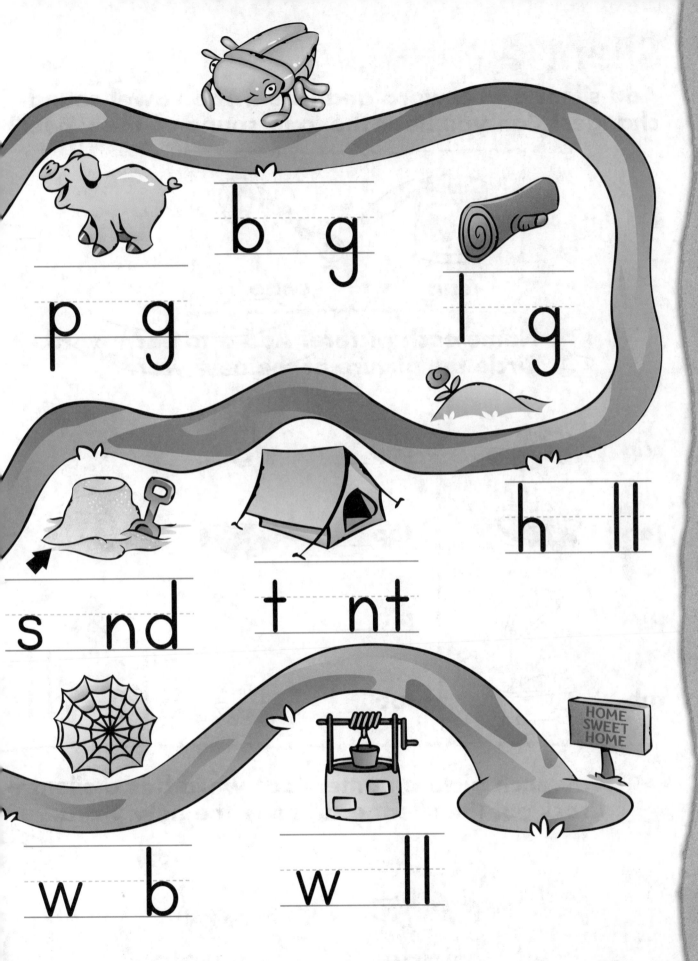

b_g

p_g

l_g

h_ll

s_nd

t_nt

w_b

w_ll

Reviewing short vowels: word maze

Silent e

Add silent e to a word and listen. The vowel sound changes! Can you hear the long sound of the vowel?

can   **cane**

 Name each picture. Add e to each word. Circle the picture of the new word.

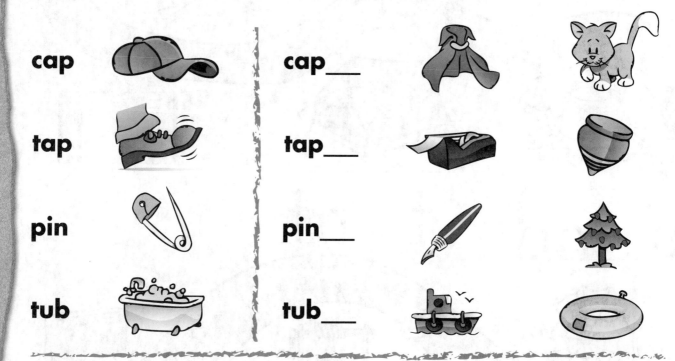

cap   cap___

tap   tap___

pin   pin___

tub   tub___

 Say each picture name. Each word has a silent e. Cross out the silent e and say the new word.

plane   **note**

238

*Adding silent **e** to words in the **CVC** pattern*

Race to the Lake

The word c**a**k**e** has the long **a** sound.

c**a**k**e**

 Help Jake get to the lake. Say each picture name. Follow and color the pictures that have the long **a** sound.

*Recognizing pictures whose names have the long sound of **a***

239

Long a and Silent e

Name each picture. Circle the picture name.
Write the word.

gate
gas

_____

- - - - - - - - - - -

_____

plane
pan

_____

- - - - - - - - - - -

_____

rat
rake

_____

- - - - - - - - - - -

_____

lake
lamp

_____

- - - - - - - - - - -

_____

tag
tape

_____

- - - - - - - - - - -

_____

snap
snake

_____

- - - - - - - - - - -

_____

Read the words in the box.
Write one word to complete the sentence.

| skate | rake | wave | bake | race |

_____

- - - - - - - - - - -

I can _____ .

Recognizing and writing words with one spelling of the long **a** sound: **a** with silent **e**

The Long Sound of ai and ay

The words train and gray have the long a sound.

Write ai to finish each long a word.

m___l   r___n

s___l   p___nt   br___d

Trace the word that completes the sentence best.

I like to play with clay   hay .

The Long Sound of ai and ay

The words **tr<u>ai</u>n** and

gr<u>ay</u> have the long **a** sound.

gray

train

Write **ai** or **ay** to finish each word.
Read the word.

ai

sn___l   p___l   t___l

ay

h___   tr___   spr___

*Spelling words with the long **a** sound: **ai** and **ay***

Rhyme Time

 and have the same ending sounds.

 and rhyme.

Name the pictures in each box.
Circle the two pictures that rhyme.

cane   **can**   **plane**

book   **cake**   **rake**

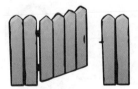      

gate   **skate**   **hat**

five   **cave**   **wave**

*Recognizing rhyming words with the long **a** sound: **a_e***

More Rhyme Time Fun

Say each picture name. Circle and then write the letter or letters that begin the second picture name. Read the words.

b (p) t

sail pail

br fr tr

gray ay

sm sn sp

trail ail

b m v

tail ail

d h r

jay ay

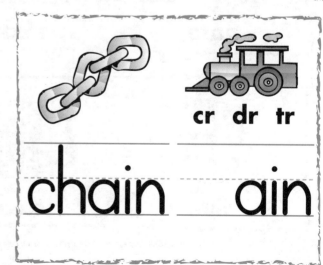

cr dr tr

chain ain

*Recognizing rhyming words with the long **a** sound: **ai** and **ay***

Puzzle It Out: Long a

Look at the picture clues. Match each picture name to a word in the box. Then write each word to finish the puzzle.

| cave | clay | nail | skate | rain | wave |

Across

2.

5.

6.

Down

1.

3.

4.

*Completing a crossword puzzle, using words with the long **a** sound: **a_e, ai,** and **ay***

VOWELS

A Piggy Picture Hunt

 Say each picture name. Then circle the 7 pictures with names that have the long a sound.

Finding hidden objects in a picture with the sound of long a

Play concentration!

play	play
clay	clay
snake	snake
rain	rain

Parents: Play concentration with two players. First cut apart the cards and place face down. The first player turns over two cards and reads each word aloud. If they match, the player wins the pair. If not, the cards are turned face down and it's the second player's turn. The player with the most word pairs wins.

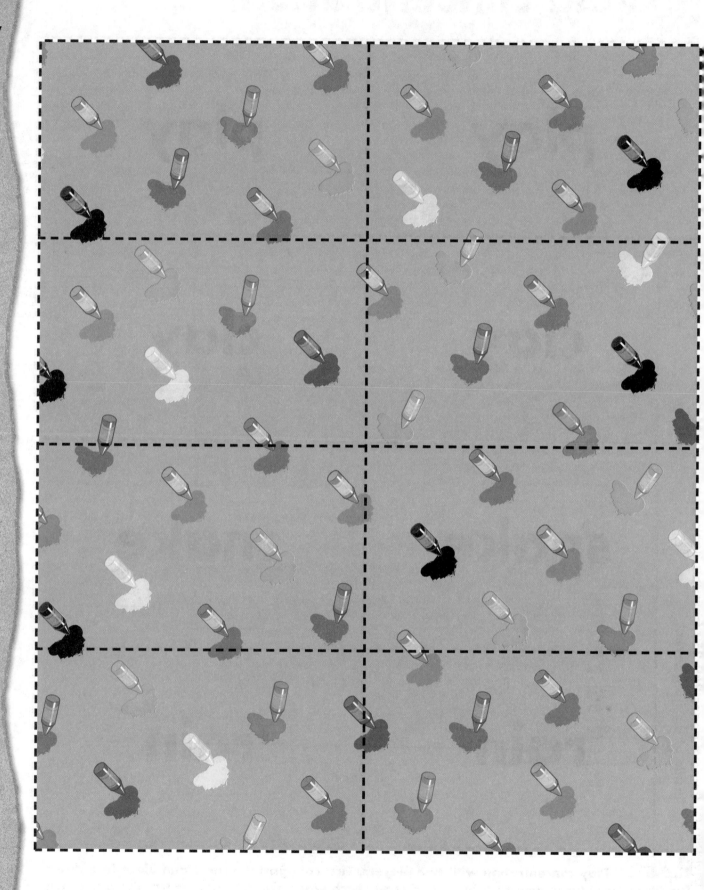

Matching words with long a

Parents: Remove pages 249-252 from this book. See directions for making mini storybooks on the inside of the front cover.

Kate and Gabe

Kate and Gabe like to play.

. . . . on this rainy day!

Kate likes to skate.

Oh, no! Look at the rain.
No more play . . .

Gabe likes to play
in the lake.

Now the snake
chases Kate.

Kate and Gabe
play with clay.
They make a
big snake!

The snake
chases Gabe.

Adding s to Words

Add s to the end of a word to show there is **more than one.**

one cat

two cats

 Count the number of things in each picture. If there is more than one, add s to the word.

 hat  sock

 car  truck

 plant  bug

 bat ball

 Circle the word for each picture.

drum   drums   horn   horns

Adding es to Words

Add **es** to words that end in **x, ss, sh,** or **ch** to show there is **more than one.**

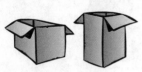  

box<u>es</u>   **dress<u>es</u>**   **dish<u>es</u>**   **witch<u>es</u>**

 Read the words in the box. Write each word beneath its matching picture. Add **es** if the picture shows more than one.

| branch | brush | fox | kiss |

baby

pat brask

 Circle the word for each picture.

bench   **benches**   **watch**   **watches**

Adding -es to form the plural

Practice Test

Say each picture name.
Fill in the circle next to the correct word.

○ sick
● snake
○ stick

● crab
○ drip
○ clap

○ car
○ snip
◉ star

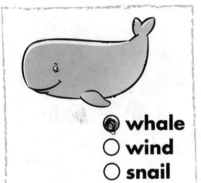
◉ whale
○ wind
○ snail

○ glad
◉ flag
○ frog

○ spread
○ draw
◉ straw

◉ cheese
○ sheep
○ sting

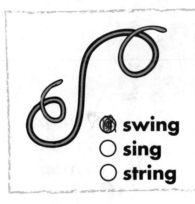
◉ swing
○ sing
○ string

○ path
○ spring
◉ thing

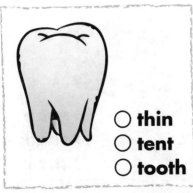
○ thin
○ tent
○ tooth

○ five
○ ship
◉ fish

◉ frog
○ trap
○ drip

Recognizing blends and digraphs

Practice Test

Say each picture name.
Fill in the circle next to the correct word.

- ○ rest
- ○ rat
- ● rake

- ○ tap
- ● tray
- ○ top

- ● plate
- ○ path
- ○ pass

- ● hat
- ○ hunt
- ○ hate

- ○ rain
- ● ran
- ○ rip

- ● clap
- ○ clay
- ○ class

- ○ man
- ○ moon
- ● mail

- ● map
- ○ main
- ○ mop

- ○ train
- ● trap
- ○ three

- ● crack
- ○ call
- ○ cake

- ○ skip
- ● sat
- ○ skate

- ○ snap
- ● snail
- ○ strap

Recognizing the short and long vowel sounds of **a**

Month 9 Checklist

Hands-on activities to help your child in school!

BLENDS & DIGRAPHS

Digraphs *ch, sh, th, wh:* page 259

Blends *sm, sn, sp, st, sw, spr;* blends with *l* and *r:* pages 260, 261

Endings *ck, ng, nt, nd:* page 262

The activities below will help you review blends and digraphs.

❏ Complete the worksheets.

❏ Give your child sheets of paper towel and crayons. Label sheet with *bl, cl, fl, gl, pl,* or *sl.* Have your child use crayons to draw a picture that begins with the blend on each sheet. Use tape to attach each sheet to a drinking straw to make blend flags. Repeat the activity with other blends.

❏ Write the word *chain* on a strip of paper that is about 4" x 1" and have your child read it. Then give your child several paper strips. Together write and then read other words that begin with *ch, sh, th,* and *wh,* one word per strip. Hook the strips together to form a word chain.

❏ Write these words on separate index cards: *pack, rock, sing, swing, plant, stand, bend.* Have your child choose a card, read the word silently, and pantomime its meaning. Can you guess the word? Switch roles with your child after each word.

VOWELS

Long *a* and short *a:* pages 264-265

Long *e:* pages 266-280

Long *e* and short *e:* page 288

This month, your child will be introduced to the long *e* sound spelled with the letters *ea* and *ee.*

❏ Complete the worksheets.

❏ Ask your child to buzz like a bee each time he or she hears you say a word that has the long *e* sound (as in *bee*). Then say the following words, one at a time: *jeep, feet, jet, dog, team, queen, nut, green, cap, lake, bike, sleep, beat, plane, ride, seed,* and *sheep.*

❑ Give your child index cards with these letters, one per card: *a, e, b, f, l, m, n, s,* and *t.* Then say a word and give your child plenty of time to use the letter cards to build and read it: *leaf, seal, meat, team, meal,* and *bean.*

❑ Remind your child that the vowel sound in *step* is short *e* and the vowel sound in *leap* is long *e.* Say the following words, one at a time: *bed, see, leg, keep, men, sleep, tent, bend, leave, get, speed, neck,* and *read.* If your child hears the short *e* sound, ask him or her to take a step backward. If he or she hears the long *e* sound, ask the child to leap forward.

WORD PARTS

Plurals: page 263
Compound Words: page 281
Prefixes *un-, re-:* pages 282, 283, 286
Endings *-ed, -ing:* pages 284, 285, 287

This month, your child will also learn about the structure of words and practice making compound words by using prefixes and suffixes.

❑ Complete the worksheets.

❑ Write the following words on separate index cards: *coat, bow, foot, base, flake, man, shine, flower, straw,* and *blue.* Have your child draw pictures of the following items on separate index cards: *rain, ball, snow, sun,* and *berry.* Place the word cards in a bag. Take turns with your child choosing a word card from the bag and matching it with a picture card to make a word. Play until all the cards are used. Tell your child that there will be two word cards that work with each picture card (*raincoat, rainbow, baseball, football, snowflake, snowman, sunshine, sunflower, strawberry, blueberry*).

❑ Print *-ed* and *-ing* on opposite sides of a plastic lid. Write the following words on separate index cards: *yell, kick, mix, plant, push, sail,* and *rest.* Take turns choosing a word card, flipping the lid, and adding the ending that is on top to the word.

❑ Have your child use objects in your home to demonstrate these word pairs: *fold/unfold, load/unload, cover/uncover, open/reopen, tie/retie, write/rewrite.*

258

Review ch, sh, th, wh

 Say each picture name. Write the letters that say its beginning sound.

ch	sh	th	wh

___ale

___ip

___umb

___ick

___eat

___eep

 Read the words in the box. Write a word to finish each phrase.

wheel	shake

_____ my hand   turn the _____

Review Beginning Blends
sm, sn, sp, st, sw, spr

Say each picture name. Write the name on the lines. Use the words in the box to help you.

step	swim	spill	snail	spring

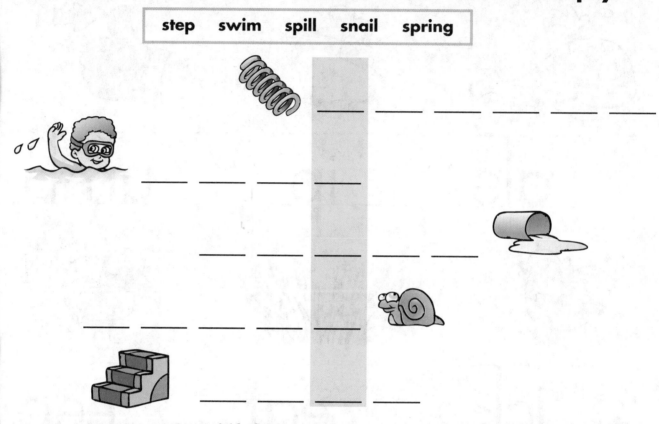

_ _ _ _ _ _

_ _ _ _

_ _ _ _ _

_ _ _ _

Look down the color strip in the puzzle above to find the missing word. Write the word to finish the rhyme.

When you walk down the street,

_____

_____ **at the people**

that you meet.

BLENDS & DIGRAPHS

Review Blends with l and r

 Look at the picture.
Follow the directions below.

bread=    **grill=**

 Draw more fruit on the table.
Draw some flowers under the tree.
Put an X on the slide.

*Reviewing initial blends with **l** and **r***

Review Endings ck, ng, nt, and nd

Help the duck get to the pond. Say each picture name. Write **ck**, **ng**, **nt**, or **nd** to finish each word.

ki**g**

chi**ck**

te**t**

ha**d**

ri**g**

ba**d**

tru

*Reviewing the sounds of **ck**, **ng**, **nt**, and **nd** at the end of words*

Review Plurals

 **Say each picture name.
Add s or es to write the plural.**

box

box

cake

cake

glass

glass

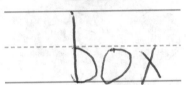

chick

chick

branch

branch

watch

watch

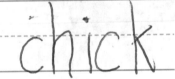

bug

bug

brush

brush

hat

hat

Reviewing the plural endings -s and -es

Riddles With Long and Short a

Write the answer to each riddle on the line below it. Use the words in the box to help you. Then draw a line from each written answer to its matching picture.

plane	cab	train

I go over rails.
I have many cars.
What am I?

_____

a _____

I go in the city.
You pay to ride in me.
What am I?

_____

a _____

I go in the sky.
I have wings.
What am I?

_____

a _____

264

Reviewing the short and long sounds of a

More Riddle Fun

  Write the answer to each riddle on the line below it. Use the words in the box to help you. Then draw a line from each written answer to its matching picture.

snail	cat	snake

**I have a shell.
I move very slowly.
What am I?**

a _____

**I crawl on the ground.
I slither and slide.
What am I?**

a _____

**I have soft fur.
I purr when I am happy.
What am I?**

a _____

Reviewing the short and long sounds of **a**

Long e

The word **sh<u>ee</u>p** has the
long e sound.

sh<u>ee</u>p

 Say each picture name.
Color the picture if you hear the long e sound.

*Recognizing pictures with names that have the long sound of **e***

Whee! Long e

  **Write ee to finish each word.
Read the word.**

 b ee

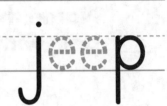 j ee p

 f ee t

 tr ee

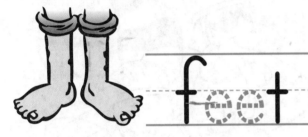 thr ee

 h ee l

 **Write a long e word to finish each sentence.**

_____

A nest is in the _____ .

_____

I see _____ birds in the nest.

Writing words with one spelling of the long e sound: double e

A Long e Treat

The word **le<u>a</u>f** has the long e sound.

leaf

 Name the animals. Color the animal in each pair with the long e sound.

Say each picture name.
Write ea to finish each word.

m _____ t   p _____ ch

p _____   b _____ n

Recognizing pictures with names that have the long e (ea) sound; writing long e (ea) words

Long e At the Beach

Write ee or ea to finish each word.
Find the pictures that show the words.
Color them. Then say the words.

j _____   p _____

l _____   f _____

tr _____   l _____

s _____

b _____   b _____ k

b _____ ch

---

*Recognizing and writing words with long **e** spelled **ee** and **ea***

269

Rhyme Time

 and  have the same ending sounds.

 and  rhyme.

 Look at the pictures. Circle the letter that begins the name of the second picture. Write that letter. Read the rhyming words.

g t (p)

f l k

sea pea

beet eet

b h m

n j p

tree ee

beach each

c s r

p t z

meal eal

heel eel

*Recognizing rhyming words with long **e** spelled **ea** and **ee***

More Rhyme Time Fun

Trace the rhyming words in each row.
Cross out the word that doesn't rhyme.

 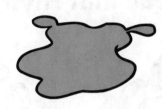 

bead   red   read

jeep   sheep   shop

  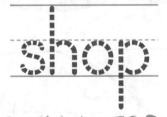

seal   meat   seat

*Recognizing rhyming words with long **e** spelled **ea** and **ee***

More Rhyme Time Fun

Look at the picture. Add one letter to the first line to make a word that names the picture. Add letters to the other lines to make words that rhyme.

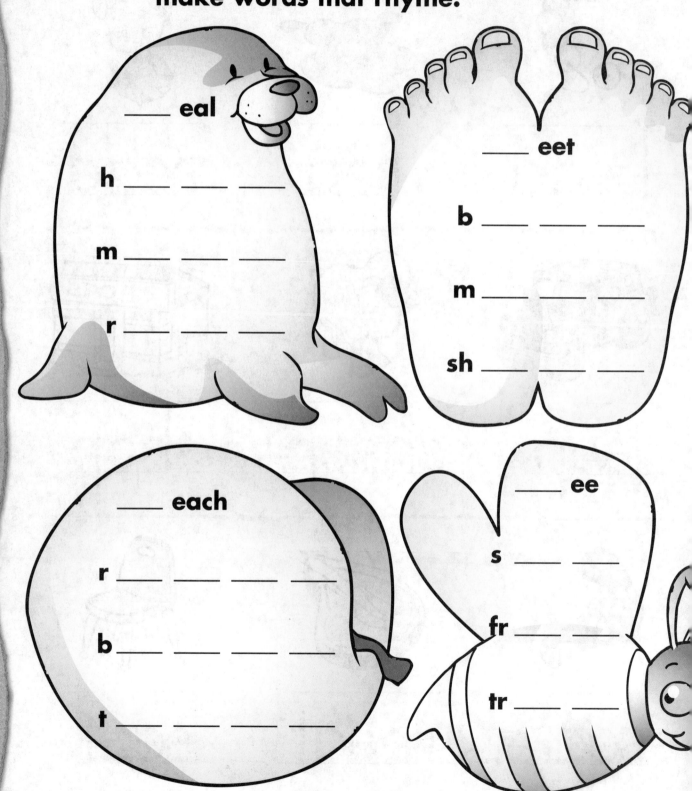

____ eal

h ____ ____ ____

m ____ ____ ____

r ____ ____ ____

____ eet

b ____ ____ ____

m ____ ____ ____

sh ____ ____ ____

____ each

r ____ ____ ____ ____

b ____ ____ ____ ____

t ____ ____ ____ ____

____ ee

s ____ ____ ____

fr ____ ____ ____

tr ____ ____ ____

*Recognizing rhyming words with long **e** spelled **ea** and **ee***

Puzzle It Out: Long e

Look at the picture clues. Match each picture name to a word in the box. Then write the word to finish the puzzle.

| feet | leaf | jeep | seal | peel | meat |

Across

1.

4.

6.

Down

2.

3.

5.

Long e

Circle 5 things in this picture with names that have the short e sound. Put an X on 5 things with names that have the long e sound.

*Finding objects with the sound of long **e** that are hidden in a picture*

Play concentration!

queen	queen
scream	scream
eat	eat
feed	feed

Parents: Play concentration with two players. First cut apart the cards and place face down. The first player turns over two cards and reads each word aloud. If they match, the player wins the pair. If not, the cards are turned face down and it's the second player's turn. The player with the most word pairs wins.

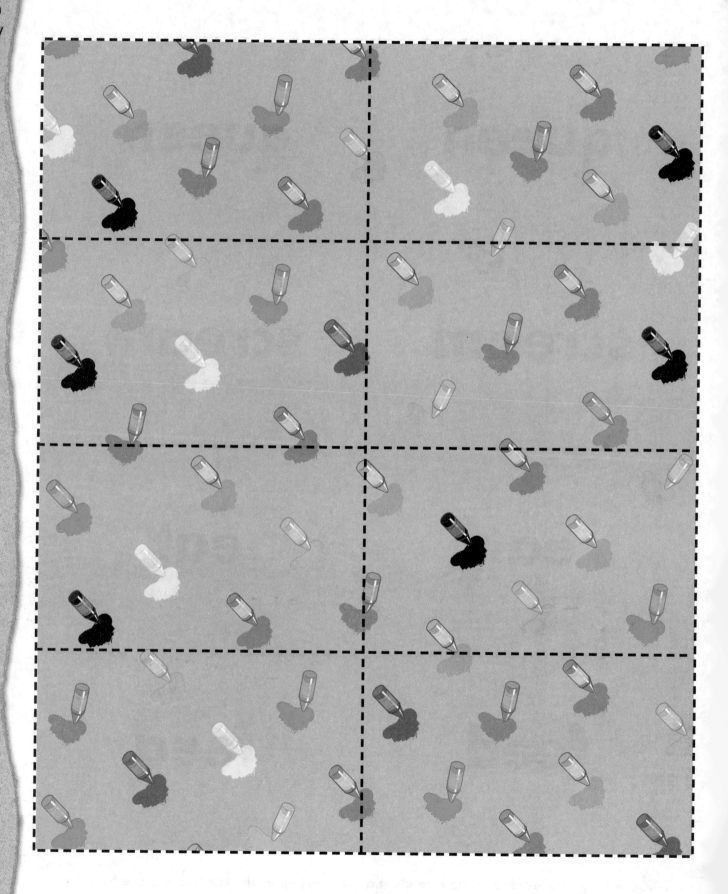

Matching words with long e

THE BEAST

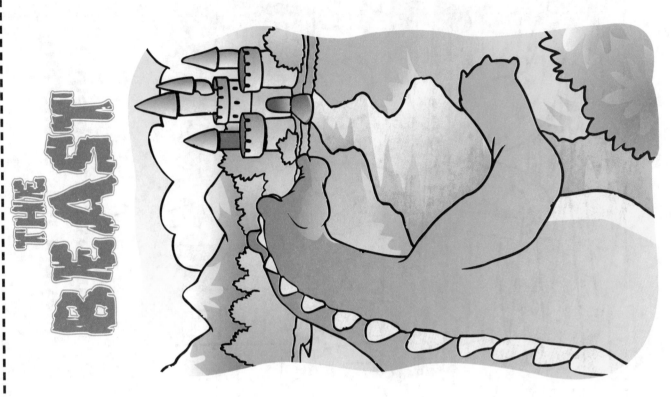

Will the beast eat seeds, wheat, or meat? No! The beast will eat this feast.

The queen sees big feet.
The queen screams!

What will a beast with
big cheeks eat?
The queen will feed him meat.

What will a beast with big feet eat?
The queen will feed him seeds.

The queen sees big cheeks.
The queen screams!

The queen sees big knees.
The queen screams!

What will a beast with
big knees eat?
The queen will feed him wheat.

Compound Words

A compound word is made from two or more shorter words.

 + = **starfish**

 + = **handbag**

Put the picture names together to make a compound word. Write it on the line.

| football   raincoat   butterfly   mailbox   pancake |

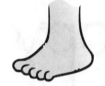 + = _____

 + = _____

 + = _____

 +  = _____

 = _____

Forming compound words from picture puzzles

Adding un to Words

Add un to the beginning of a word to make a new word.

load   **un + load = unload**

 Look at the pictures. Add un to finish the word.

happy       happy

pack    pack

safe    safe

wrap     wrap

_____ *Adding the prefix* **un-** _____

Adding re to Words

Add re to the beginning of a word to make a new word.

tie

Oops!

re + tie = retie

 Look at the pictures. Add re to finish the word.

build

Oops!

_____ build

wash

Oops!

_____ wash

use

Oops!

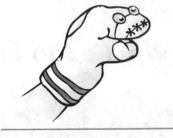
_____ use

Adding ed to Words

Add **ed** to a word to show you did it in the past:
walk + ed = walked

Lil walked the dog.

Look at the picture.
Add the ending ed to finish the word.

Dad ____wash____ **the van.**

Mom __fix__ **the gate.**

Ann ___paint___ **the fence.**

Bob __mow__ **the grass.**

Write ed to finish the word.

Then they all __rest__ **.**

Adding the inflectional ending -ed

Adding ing to Words

Add ing to a word to show you are doing it now.
plant + ing = planting

I am **planting** bean seeds.

 Look at the picture. Add the ending **ing** to the word to make a new word.
Read the new word.

water _____

grow _____

pick _____

cook _____

eat _____

Practice Test

Look at the picture. Fill in the circle next to un or re. Write un or re at the beginning of the word.

○ un
○ re

_____ happy

○ un
○ re

_____ safe

○ un
○ re

_____ use

○ un
○ re

_____ fill

286 ——————————————— *Recognizing the prefixes **un-** and **re-*** ———————————————

More Practice

 Say each picture name. Add ed or ing to make a new word.

play   row   jump

splash   kick   melt

rain   fish   sleep

Practice Test II

  Say each picture name. Fill in the circle next to the correct word. Color each picture that has the long e sound in its name.

○ beg
● beak

○ jet
● jeep

○ mean
● men

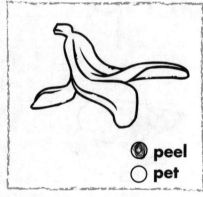
● peel
○ pet

○ leg
● leaf

○ bee
● bed

● hen
○ heel

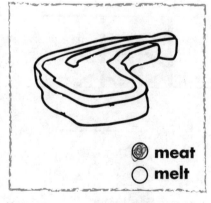
● meat
○ melt

○ neat
● nest

⊘ weed
● web

● bee
○ bell

○ ten
● team

*Recognizing the short and long vowel sounds of **e***

Month 10 Checklist

Hands-on activities to help your child in school!

WORD PARTS

Prefixes *un-* and *re-*; endings with *-ed* and *-ing*: pages 291–292

Compound Words: pages 295–296

Contractions with *not*, *are*, and *will*: pages 316–319

How do the prefixes *un-* and *re-* change the meaning of words? How are *-ed* and *-ing* used to show past and present tense? When can two short words be combined to form a new word (compound)? How are contractions used? All of these questions are answered in this month's work.

❑ Complete the worksheets.

❑ Put on a jacket or sweater with buttons and have your child put one on, too. Say *button*, and begin buttoning your jacket. Have your child do the same. As you both are buttoning, say the word *buttoning*. Have your child repeat the word. When finished, say *buttoned*. Have your child repeat it. Then, unbutton the jacket. When you are done, say *unbuttoned* and have your child copy you. Finally, rebutton the jacket and say the word *rebutton*. Repeat the activity, having your child call out the words *buttoning*, *buttoned*, *unbuttoned*, and *rebutton*.

❑ Make or buy two cupcakes. Write the word *cupcake* on a piece of paper and ask your child to read it aloud. Ask which two small words make up the compound word *cupcake*. Then, read a book with your child, stopping when you come upon a compound word. Challenge your child to find the two words that make up the compound. If correct, allow your child to take a bite of the cupcake. Continue until the cupcake is all gone. (It is helpful to make a list of the compound words you encounter for later reference.)

❑ Make contraction flash cards. Write the following word pairs on one side of an index card, and write the matching contraction on the flip side: *we will/we'll, they will/they'll, we are/we're, they are/they're, you are/you're, do not/don't, will not/won't, can not/can't*. Show your child the word pair on an index card and challenge him or her to name the contraction on the flip side. Once you've reviewed all cards, reverse the process. Show your child the contraction side of the flash card, and challenge him or her to name the two words it stands for. Extend the activity with these additional contractions: *he will/he'll, she will/she'll, you will/you'll, did not/didn't, are not/aren't*.

CONSONANTS

Words Beginning with soft *c*, soft *g*: pages 293–294

To review soft vowel sounds:

❑ Complete the worksheets.

❑ Pour out some cereal. Explain that the word *cereal* begins with the soft *c* sound. With pieces of cereal, spell out—one word at a time—*cent, cider, cell, center, cement, circus, circle, and city* and challenge your child to read the words aloud. To extend the activity, mix up the cereal pieces, say a word, and guide your child in spelling it out with the cereal. You can play the same game to explore words that begin with soft *g*. Use these words: *gym, germ, gerbil, giant, gel, gem.*

VOWELS

Long Vowel *i*: pages 297–312, 314, 320
Vowel Sounds of *y*: page 313
Long Vowel *e*: page 315

This month, your child will be introduced to the long *i* sound represented by these letters and letter combinations: *ie* (as in *tie*), *y* (as in *cry*), *igh* (as in *night*), and *i_e* (as in *nine* and *kite*). The sound of *y*, as in *funny*, will also be presented. Use the activities below to help reinforce your child's understanding of long *i* words and the two sounds of *y*:

❑ Complete the worksheets.

❑ Make a "Long *i* Kite." Cut out a large piece of paper in the shape of a kite. Provide drawing materials and ask your child to draw pictures of things with the long *i* sound such as a *bike, hike, sky, bride, slide, light, pipe, and mice.* When your child is finished, help him or her tape the long *i* pictures to the Long *i* Kite.

❑ Write *e* and *i* on two separate index cards. Say a number of words to your child that end in *y*. Have him or her hold up the *e* card if the *y* makes the sound of long *e* and the *i* card if the *y* makes the sound of long *i*. Use these words: *bunny, city, cry, dry, funny, merry, pony, sky, try.* Add words of your own.

Review: un and re

In each box, draw lines from the words to the pictures they match.

happy   unhappy

painted   unpainted

opened   unopened

tied   untied

Look at the three pictures.
Write un or re to finish each word.

locked

_____ locked

_____ locked

Review: ed and ing

Look at the pictures. Write a word from the box to finish each sentence.

fixed opened drawing running sleeping

Mom _____ **Ann's toy.**

Lisa is _____ **a dog.**

Pat is _____ **up a hill.**

The pups are _____ **.**

Kim _____ **the jar of jam.**

Reviewing the inflectional endings -ed and -ing

Review Hard and Soft c

What is in the cellar? Say each picture name.
If it begins with a hard c like , color it .
If it begins with a soft c like , color it .

Say each picture name.
Write the word that matches the picture.

| cent | cow | circus |

_____

Review: Hard and Soft g

Say the name of the picture in the box. Say the names of the other two pictures in the row. Circle the picture with the same sound of g.

giant	goose	giraffe
girl	gate	gym
game	giraffe	goggles
gem	gym	goat
garden	gerbil	gold
goose	gem	goldfish

Reviewing the hard and soft sounds of g

Compound Words

A compound word is a word made from two or more shorter words.

 + =

snow + **man** = **snowman**

 Say the picture names in each box.
Write the compound word.

 +  = _____

pin + **wheel** = _____

 +  =  _____

tea + **pot** = _____

 +  = _____

cup + **cake** = _____

 +  = _____

dog + **house** = _____

 +  =  _____

star + **fish** = _____

Compound Words

 Look at the pictures on the left. Read the first part of the word. Draw a line to the second part of the compound word.

pig   paper

bed   hive

news   box

sail   pen

sand   boat

bee   room

Slide into Long i

The word slid<u>e</u> has the long i sound.

slid<u>e</u>

 Say each picture name.
Color the picture if you hear the long i sound.

Time for Long i

Say each picture name. Circle the picture with the long i sound in its name. Trace i and e to finish each word. Read the word.

tire

dime

vine

kite

Mike **on a** bike

Recognizing and writing words with one spelling of the long i sound: i with silent e

A Pie of Long i

The word **pie** has the long **i** sound.

 Say each picture name. Trace only the words with the long i sound.

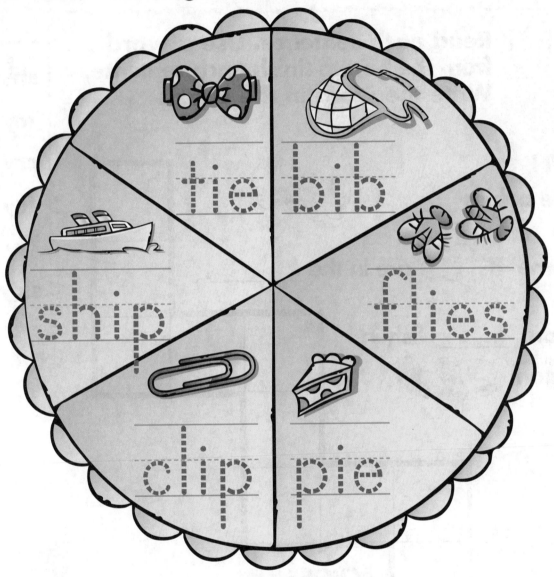

tie bib

ship

flies

clip pie

Read the word. Circle the picture that matches the word.

pie

tie

*Recognizing and writing words with long **i** spelled **ie***

Try Long i

The word **fly** has the long
i sound.

fl<u>y</u>

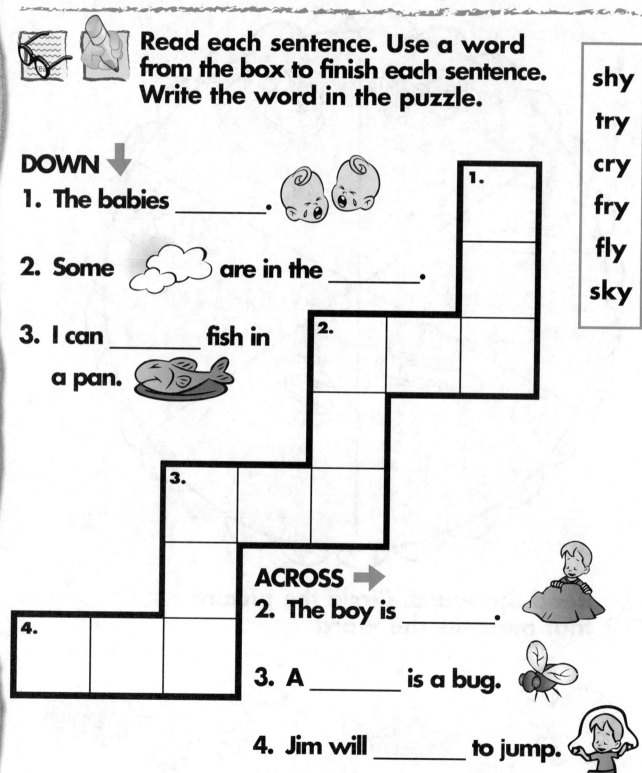

Read each sentence. Use a word
from the box to finish each sentence.
Write the word in the puzzle.

shy

try

cry

fry

fly

sky

DOWN

1. The babies _____.

2. Some ☁ are in the _____.

3. I can _____ fish in
   a pan.

ACROSS

2. The boy is _____.

3. A _____ is a bug.

4. Jim will _____ to jump.

*Using words with one spelling of the long **i** sound: **y***

More Words with Long i

The words **b<u>i</u>k<u>e</u>** , **p<u>ie</u>** , and **sk<u>y</u>** have the long **i** sound.

These shirts are out to dry. Say the picture name on each shirt. Then draw a line to the word it matches.

spy   bike   tie

pipe   pie   cry

Say each picture name. Write the missing letters to finish each word.

t _____   f ____ v ____   sk ____

Rhyme Time

The words **fire** 🔥 , **tie** 🎀 , and **sky** ☁ have the long **i** sound.

 Say the picture names in each box.
Trace the two words that rhyme.

five   drip   dive

cry   pie   crib

ship   sky   fly

*Recognizing rhyming words with long **i** spelled **i_e**, **ie**, and **y***

More Rhyme Time Fun

 Say each picture name. Write the missing word to make words that rhyme.

cry	kite	tie	bride	mice	dime

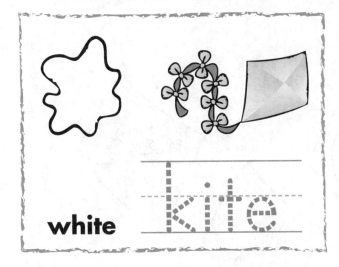

white   kite

pie

lime

sky

price

slide

*Recognizing rhyming words with long **i** spelled **i_e**, **ie**, and **y***

Even More <u>More</u> Rhyme Time Fun!

 The kites need string! Say the picture name on each kite. Draw a string to the  wearing the word that rhymes with the picture.

*Recognizing rhyming words with long **i** spelled **i_e** and **ie***

Puzzle It Out: Long i

Say each picture name. Write the word for each picture. Then read the secret word in the box. Write the word beside its picture.

| dive | cry | pie | dime |

A Sidewalk Picture Hunt

Find and circle at least 7 things in this picture that have the long i sound.

OPEN
9 till 5

Finding objects with the sound of long i that are hidden in a picture

Play concentration!

nine	**nine**
mice	**mice**
hide	**hide**
like	**like**

Parents: Play concentration with two players. First cut apart the cards and place face down. The first player turns over two cards and reads each word aloud. If they match, the player wins the pair. If not, the cards are turned face down and it's the second player's turn. The player with the most word pairs wins.

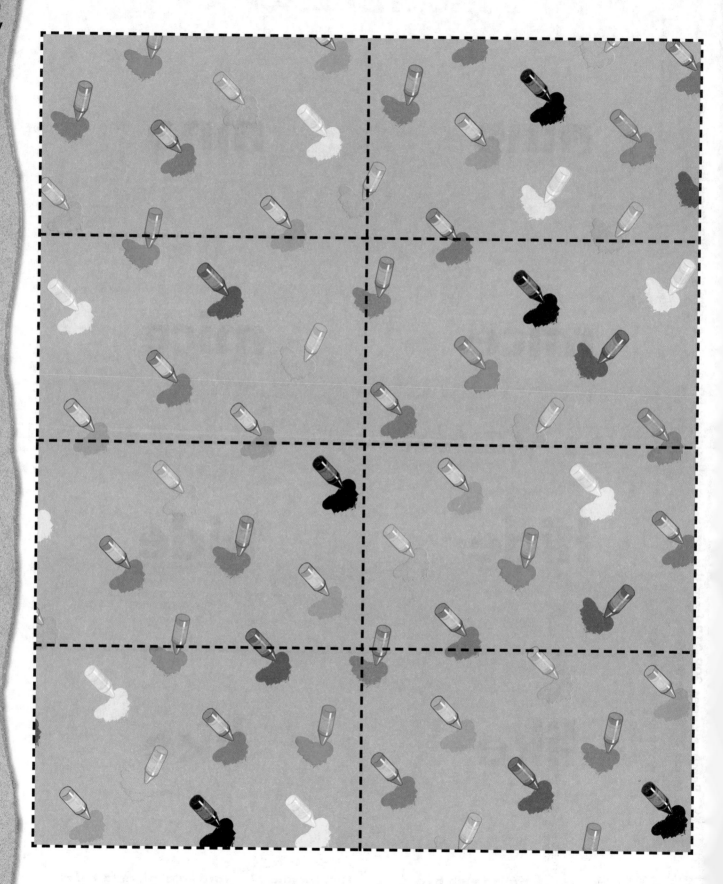

Matching words with long **i**

Parents: Remove pages 309-312 from this book. See directions for making mini storybooks on the inside of the front cover.

Find The Mice!

Nine mice are in bed.
They are tired of hiding!

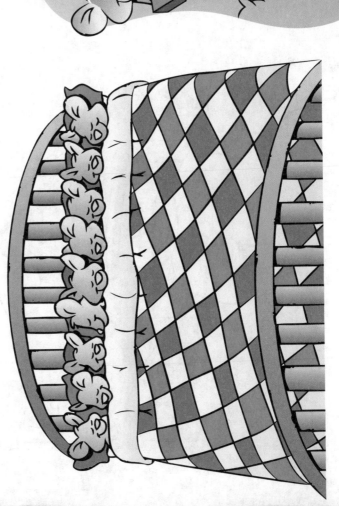

Mice like to hide.
Can you find them?

Three mice hide in
the snow.
Find the mice!

Five mice hide in the tree. Find the mice!

Three mice hide in the class. Find the mice!

Aa Bb Cc

Three mice hide in
the shop.
Find the mice!

Nine mice hide in
the pipes.
Find the mice!

Vowel Sounds of y

The letter **y** in **bunny**  makes the long **e** sound.

The letter **y** in **fly**  makes the long **i** sound.

 **Say each picture name. If it ends like bunny, write an e on the line. If it ends like fly, write an i on the line.**

pony

_____

- - - - - - - - - -

_____

sky

_____

- - - - - - - - - -

_____

dry

_____

- - - - - - - - - -

_____

funny

_____

- - - - - - - - - -

_____

cry

_____

- - - - - - - - - -

_____

city

_____

- - - - - - - - - -

_____

 Color the picture that matches the word.

dry

ugly

Long Sound of igh

The letters igh in light  **make a long i sound.**

 Write igh to finish each word.
Draw a line to the picture it matches.

l _____ t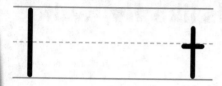

h _____

t _____ t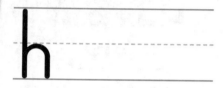

n _____ t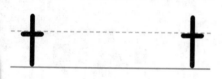

fr _____ t

f _____ t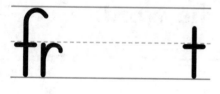

314

Recognizing words with long i spelled igh

VOWELS

Riddles with Short and Long e

**Look at each picture.
Read the riddle. Write the answer.**

| bed | queen | bench | street | read |

Cars drive here. _____

You do this with a book. _____

She wears a crown. _____

You sleep in me. _____

You sit on me in the park. _____

Contractions with not

A contraction is a way of putting two words together and making them shorter.	Sometimes the first word changes.
do + not = don't **Do not** go in my room. **Don't** go in my room.	will + not = won't I **will not** go in your room. I **won't** go in your room.

 **Look at puzzle words on the left.
Color the puzzle piece on the right that matches.**

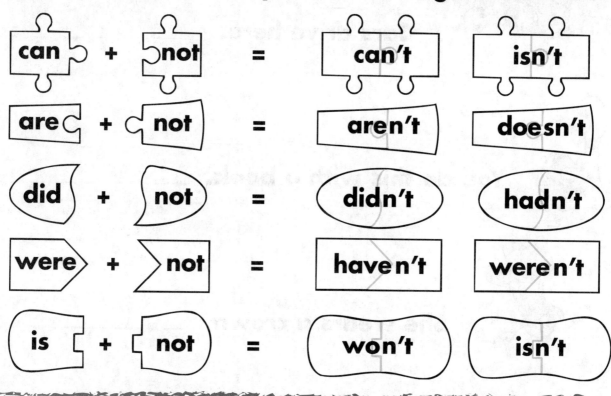

can + not = can't   isn't

are + not = aren't   doesn't

did + not = didn't   hadn't

were + not = haven't   weren't

is + not = won't   isn't

  **Trace the contraction in each box.
Then circle the two words that it
comes from.**

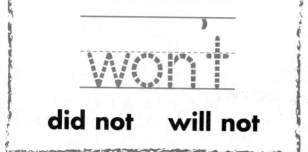

won't

did not   will not

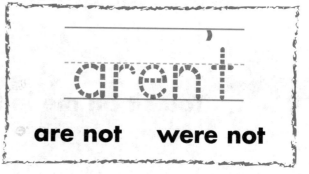

aren't

are not   were not

Contractions with are

A contraction is a way of putting two words together and making them shorter.	We + are = we're We are going to the zoo. We're going to the zoo.

 Read the first sentence. Write They're, We're, or You're to finish the second sentence.

We are going to the beach!

_____

_____ going to the beach!

They are in the water.

_____

_____ in the water.

You are reading!

_____

_____ reading!

 Read the contraction in each box. Circle the words it comes from.

we're	**they're**	**you're**
we are you are	you are they are	you are we are

Contractions with will

A contraction is a way of putting two words together and making them shorter.

I + will = I'll
I will eat my lunch.
I'll eat my lunch.

 Look at the contraction under each frog. Make the frog hop to the words it matches.

we'll

we   they

will

you'll

he   you

will

he'll

we   he

will

they'll

they   who

will

Practice Test

 Read the first two words in each box. Then fill in the circle beside the contraction that matches.

can not
- ○ didn't
- ○ won't
- ● can't

you are
- ○ you're
- ○ you'll
- ○ we're

did not
- ○ don't
- ○ didn't
- ○ doesn't

they are
- ○ they're
- ○ you're
- ○ they'll

do not
- ○ don't
- ○ didn't
- ○ doesn't

we are
- ○ we'll
- ○ we're
- ○ he'll

she will
- ○ he'll
- ○ she'll
- ○ we'll

they will
- ○ they're
- ○ she'll
- ○ they'll

we are
- ○ we're
- ○ we'll
- ○ you're

had not
- ○ didn't
- ○ won't
- ○ hadn't

you will
- ○ you're
- ○ you'll
- ○ we'll

will not
- ○ won't
- ○ didn't
- ○ can't

*Recognizing contractions with **not**, **are**, and **will***

Practice Test

Say the picture name.
Fill in the circle next to the correct word.

- ○ peg
- ○ bike
- ● pig

- ○ pie
- ● pit
- ○ pill

- ● bench
- ○ big
- ○ bike

- ○ bag
- ○ big
- ● bite

- ○ cheek
- ● chick
- ○ check

- ○ pop
- ● pipe
- ○ pup

- ○ dent
- ○ dim
- ● dime

- ● light
- ○ lost
- ○ lid

- ○ drill
- ○ drip
- ● drape

- ○ flag
- ● flip
- ○ flop

- ○ kit
- ○ keep
- ● kite

- ○ flip
- ● fly
- ○ tie

320

Recognizing the short and long vowel sounds of **i**

Month 11 Checklist

Hands-on activities to help your child in school!

VOWELS

Vowel sounds of *y*: page 323
Short and Long *i*: page 329
Long *o*: pages 330-337, 339-344
Short and Long *o*: pages 330, 338, 350
Sounds of *ow*: page 345
Vowel Combinations: pages 346-347, 351

This month, your child continues work on long vowels with the introduction of the long *o* sound spelled *o_e*, *oa*, and *ow*. Activities that provide practice in other vowel combinations are also reviewed.

❑ Complete the worksheets.

❑ Ask your child to pantomime rowing a boat each time you say a word that has the long *o* sound (as in *row* and *boat*). Use the following words: *top, road, goat, bike, note, snow, cat, bone, woke, mow, toad.*

❑ Have your child draw a boat on a large sheet of paper, and then cut pictures from magazines that have the long *o* sound (as in boat) and glue them inside the boat.

❑ Take out a brown bag and a plastic bowl. Review that the letters *ow* can stand for the vowel sound in *brown* or the long *o* sound in *bowl*. Write these words on separate index cards, one word per card: *snow, bow, crow, row, mow, clown, town, gown, frown,* and *crown.* Help your child read each word, underline the letters *ow*, and then place the words that have the vowel sound in *brown* in the brown bag and the words that have the long *o* sound in *bowl* in the bowl.

❑ Write the vowel combinations *ou, ow, oi,* and *oy* on separate index cards. Give your child these letter cards: *h, s, e, c, h, m, t, l, f, r, b,* and *n.* Ask your child to add the letter cards to the beginning and end of the vowel combinations to build words. For example: *house, mouse, blouse, mouth, south, cow, how, brown, frown, clown, coin, foil, boil, oil, boy,* and *toy.*

WORD PARTS

Compound Words: page 324
Contractions: page 325
Syllabication: pages 326-328; 352
Homophones: pages 348-349

In addition to reviewing compound words and contractions, the syllable—a word or word part with one vowel sound—is introduced this month. Words can have one or more syllables: for example, the word *fish* has one syllable, the word *wagon* has two, and the word *kangaroo* has three. Homophones, words that sound alike but have different spellings and meanings, such as *right* and *write*, are also presented.

❏ Complete the worksheets.

❏ Help your child use a red marker to print *suit, week, sand, play,* and *bean* and a black marker to print *case, end, box, pen,* and *bag* on index cards, one word per card. Place the red words and black words in separate piles. Match a red word with a black word to make a compound.

❏ Write the letters for *are not* on cards, one letter per card. Using a piece of elbow macaroni as an apostrophe, have your child make the contraction *aren't* by taking away the letter o and putting the apostrophe in its place. Repeat with other contractions, such as *I will (I'll), she will (she'll), can not (can't), is not (isn't), you are (you're),* and *we are (we're).*

❏ Write the following words on index cards, one word per card, leaving space so that your child can cut between syllables: *bas ket, rab bit, puz zle, tur key, kit ten,* and *but ter.* Read each word aloud. Then have your child repeat the word, clap once for each word part or syllable, and cut the words between syllables. Extend the activity by mixing up the cards that have been cut. Then have your child find and join two cards that, when put together, make up a word. Have the child read the word aloud.

❏ Write homophone pairs on self-stick notes, one word per note. Tag objects in your home with one word of the pair and give the other word to your child to match with its homophone. Some household items you might tag are *wood, cent, clothes, pail, flour, bear (teddy), pane (window),* and *mail.* The matching homophones to give to your child are: *would, sent, close, pale, flower, bare, pain,* and *male.*

322

Review y Sounds

 Look at each picture and its name. Draw a line to the fly if y has the long i sound. **Draw a line to the bunny** if y has the long e sound.

fly

cry

pony

dry

sky

city

penny

bunny

Review Compound Words

Write a compound word to answer each clue.

shoelace wishbone goldfish popcorn backpack

a **bone** you **wish** on _____

corn that goes **"Pop!"** _____

a **pack** you put on your **back** _____

a **lace** you have in your **shoe** _____

a **fish** that is **gold** _____

Review Contractions

Write the contraction for the two underlined words. The words in the box will help you.

| We're | isn't | I'll | can't | You'll |

_____

_____

_____
We are   going to a farm.

_____

_____

_____
You will   ride a pony.

_____

_____

_____
I will   feed the goats.

_____

_____

We _____ jump in the haystack.
        can not

_____

_____

Hay _____ for us.
        is not

Hay is for cows!

Count the Syllables

Say **cap**.   Clap it out.   The word **cap** has **1** syllable.
Say **monkey**. Clap it out.   The word **monkey** has 2 syllables.
Say **bicycle**. Clap it out.   The word **bicycle** has 3 syllables.

 Say each picture name. Clap it out. Color a block for each syllable that you hear.

	/ /		
	/ / /		
	/ / /		
	/ /		
	/ /		
	/ / /		

Counting syllables

Words with Two Syllables

has two syllables.
zip-per

has two syllables.
tur-key

 Name each picture. Connect the pictures whose names have 2 syllables, making a path that forms the number 2.

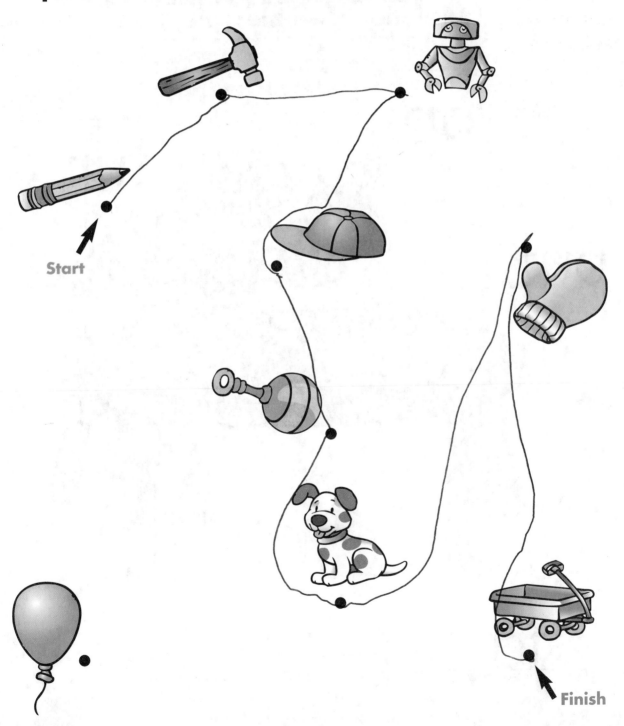

Start

Finish

Recognizing how to divide words into syllables between consonants; counting syllables

Syllables with –le

 has two parts: **can-dle.**

 Write a syllable from the box to finish each word.

tle zle ble ple

ap _____

puz _____

tur _____

ta _____

Recognizing how to divide words with -le into syllables

Short and Long i Riddles

Draw a line from the riddle to the matching picture. Write the answer on the line. The words in the box will help you.

hill	crib	hive

It has four sides.
A baby sleeps here.
What is it?

_____

- - - - - - - - - - - - ●

It is a _____ .

Jack and Jill went up it.
You can roll down it.
What is it?

_____

- - - - - - - - - - - - ●

It is a _____ .

You might find honey here.
Bees live in it.
What is it?

_____

- - - - - - - - - - - - ●

It is a _____ .

Reviewing the short and long sounds of **i**

Long o or Short o

The word **r<u>o</u>s<u>e</u>** has the long **o** sound.

rose

 Say each picture name.
Do you hear the long **o** sound?

Color if you do. Color 😞 if you do not.

Distinguishing between the long and short sounds of **o**

Crack the Code

 Write o and e to finish each word. Draw a line to match each word with its picture.

note

home

robe

cone

globe

Reach Your Goal with Long o

The word b**oa**t  has the long **o** sound.

b**oa**t

 Write the words on the correct pictures.

| soap | toad | coat | goat |

 Draw a line from the words to the matching picture.

a toad on the road

a goat in a boat

*Recognizing and writing words with one spelling of the long **o** sound: **oa***

Do You Know Long o?

The word **b<u>ow</u>** has the long **o** sound.

 Color the bow red. Color the crow black. Draw a sled in the snow.

 Write two words that have the long o sound spelled ow.

_____   _____

_____   _____

Rhyme Time

 and  have the same ending sounds.

 and ⛵ rhyme.

goat boat

Look at each picture. Write two rhyming words from the box to describe the picture.

| toad | show | mole | road | crow | hole |

_____   _____

_____   _____

_____   _____

Completing rhymes using words with long ●

More Rhyme Time Fun

Write words that rhyme with crow on the crow, with oak on the oak tree, and with cone on the ice cream cone.

| soak | grow | bone | croak | stone | blow |

Even More Rhyme Time Fun!

Write a word from the box to finish each rhyme.

cone	rose	slow	float

**Do you know
why a snail goes**

_____

- - - - - - - - - - - - - - -

_____ ?

**I sniff with my nose
this sweet smelling**

_____

- - - - - - - - - - - - - - -

_____ .

**Fix this boat
so it can**

_____

- - - - - - - - - - - - - - -

_____ .

**In this work zone
is an orange**

_____

- - - - - - - - - - - - - - -

_____ .

Completing rhymes using words with long o

Puzzle It Out: Long o

Find each picture name in the box. Then write it in the puzzle grid.

toad	boat	snow	note	toast	road

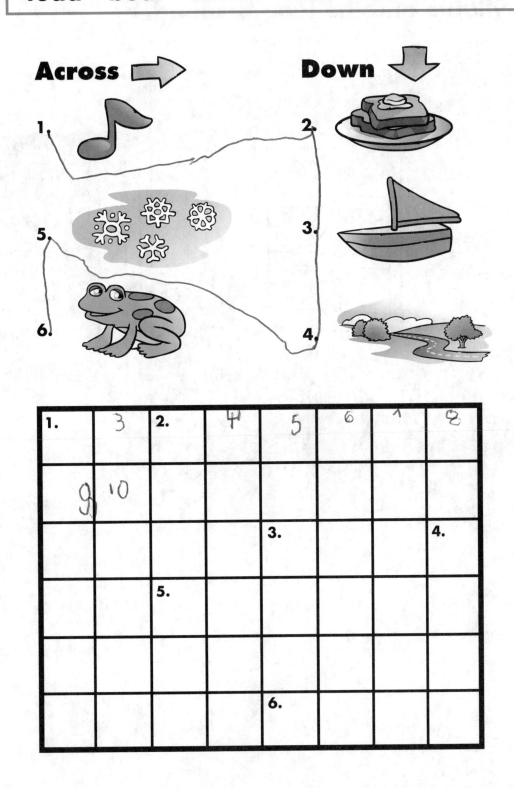

Across ➡

1.

5.

6.

Down ⬇

2.

3.

4.

A Puppy Picture Hunt

 Circle 5 things in this picture that have one syllable and the short o sound.

 Put an X on at least 5 things that have one syllable and the long o sound.

Finding an object with the sound of short o or long o hidden in a picture; recognizing one syllable words

Play concentration!

those	**those**
hole	**hole**
know	**know**
snow	**snow**

Parents: Play concentration with two players. First cut apart the cards and place facedown. The first player turns over two cards and reads each word aloud. If they match, the player wins the pair. If not, the cards are turned face down and it's the second player's turn. The player with the most word pairs wins.

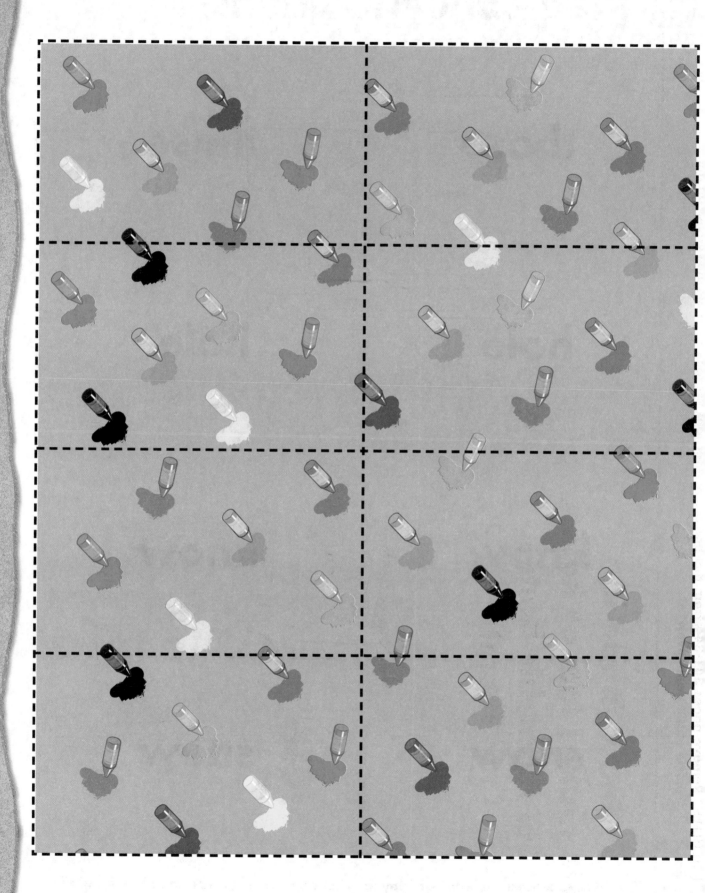

Matching words with long o

Lots of Holes

Snow made it!
He makes lots of holes.
He hides his bones
in them!

Look at these holes!

Who made this hole?
Do you know?

Who made this hole?
Do you know?

A mole makes this hole.
It will make a home
in this hole.

Mom made this hole.
She plants an oak tree
in this hole.

Who makes this hole?
Do you know?

Sounds of ow

The letters **ow** can stand for the vowel sound in **clown** or the long **o** sound in **bow** .

 Color the picture if the word has the vowel sound in **clown**.

Circle long **o** if it has the sound in **bow**.

row

long o

gown

long o

town

long o

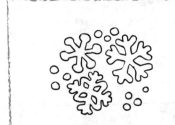

snow

long o

crown

long o

throw

long o

cow

long o

mow

long o

frown

long o

Sound of ou and ow

The **ou** in **c<u>ou</u>ch** and the **ow** in **cr<u>ow</u>n** have the same sound.

Write each word on the line near its picture.

cloud	house	cow	flower	hound

Identifying words with the vowel combinations: **ou** *and* **ow**

Sound of oi and oy

The **oi** in <u>co</u>ins and the **oy** in b<u>oy</u> have the same sound.

 Unscramble the letters. Write the **oi** or **oy** word from the box that names each picture.

| boy | foil | toy | point | coins | Roy |

l i f o

_____

o y t

_____

n o i c s

_____

o R y

_____

t n o p i

_____

y o b

_____

 Look at the picture. Write **oy** and **oi** words from above to finish the sentence.

The _____ puts _____ in his bank.

Sound-Alikes

Some words sound alike but have different spellings and meanings.

I like my **blue** cap.
The wind **blew** my cap off my head.

Blue is the name of a color.
Blew means "carried away."

 Write the word that names each picture.

sail
sale
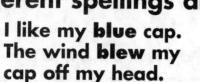

see
sea
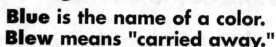

beat
beet

road
rode

pear
pair

plane
plain

Write two words from the boxes above to answer each riddle.

What do you call a tired vegetable?

a _____ _____

What do you call two friendly fruits?

a _____ of _____ S

Recognizing and writing homophones

More Sound-Alikes

 Draw lines to connect the words that sound alike.

meet   **tale**   **son**   **read**

tail   **red**   **meat**   **sun**

 Write the word that finishes each sentence.

_____

Mom _____ me a funny story.   **read**
red

_____   **meet**

Two pigs _____ on a farm.   **meat**

_____   **son**

The pigs sit in the _____ .   **sun**

_____   **tales**

The pigs try to curl their _____ .   **tails**

Recognizing and writing homophones

349

Practice Test

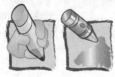 **Say each picture name. Fill in the circle next to the correct word. Color each picture that has the long o sound in its name.**

- ● coat
- ○ cot

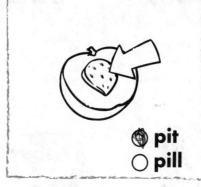
- ◉ pit
- ○ pill

- ○ rob
- ◉ robe

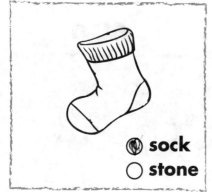
- ◉ sock
- ○ stone

- ○ not
- ◉ note

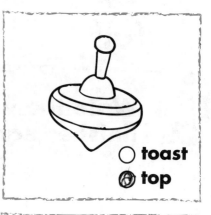
- ○ toast
- ◉ top

- ○ hot
- ◉ hose

- ◉ clock
- ○ coach

- ◉ bowl
- ○ boat

- ○ doe
- ◉ dog

- ○ sock
- ◉ snow

- ◉ pot
- ○ poke

Recognizing the short and long vowel sounds of o

Practice Test

 Say each picture name. Fill in the circle next to the correct word.

● gown
○ grow

○ clock
◉ cloud

◉ toy
◉ town

○ croak
○ crown

◉ oil
○ owl

○ coat
◉ couch

◉ paint
◉ point

◉ boy
◉ boil

◉ clam
◉ clown

◉ mouse
◉ mole

◉ cot
◉ coins

◉ Roy
○ row

Recognizing vowel combinations

351

Practice Test

 Say each picture name. Fill in the circle next to the number of word parts or syllables you hear.

○ 1
○ 2
● 3

◉ 1
○ 2
○ 3

○ 1
◉ 2
○ 3

○ 1
◉ 2
○ 3

◉ 1
○ 2
○ 3

◉ 1
○ 2
○ 3

◉ 1
○ 2
○ 3

◉ 1
○ 2
○ 3

◉ 1
○ 2
○ 3

◉ 1
○ 2
○ 3

◉ 1
○ 2
○ 3

◉ 1
○ 2
○ 3

Recognizing syllables in words

Month 12 Checklist

Hands-on activities to help your child in school!

WORD PARTS

Syllabication: page 355
Homophones: pages 356, 379

This month, your child will continue to learn about word parts or syllables and homophones (words that sound alike but are spelled differently and have different meanings).

❑ Complete the worksheets.

❑ Place several objects with names that are made up of one, two, or three syllables on a table. Have your child say the name of each object and clap once for each syllable. Some common items to use include: can, dish, letter, basket, telephone, handkerchief.

❑ Print the numerals 1, 2, and 3 on separate self-stick notes. Help your child tag each note to an object in your home or yard that has a matching number of syllables.

❑ Point to a picture in a favorite storybook and ask your child to say its name and then tell you the number of word parts or syllables in its name.

❑ Make word cards for at least four pairs of homophones, one card per word. For example: *see/sea, son/sun, road/rode, and meet/meat*. Mix up the cards and lay them facedown on a table in a 4x4 grid. Take turns turning over two cards at a time to make homophone matches. As a challenge, when a match is made, work together to use each word correctly in a sentence.

VOWELS

Review Vowel Combinations: page 357

Long *u*: pages 358–372

Short and Long *u*: page 380

Short and Long *o*: page 374

Sounds of *oo*: page 373

Short and Long Vowels: pages 375–378, 381

Long Vowels: page 382

The following activities will help your child practice identifying vowel sounds.

❑ Complete the worksheets.

❑ Save the cardboard tube from a paper towel roll. Show your child how to use a marker to draw pictures of objects whose names have the long *u* sound, as in *tube*, on the cardboard. Invite your child to play a tune with the decorated "Tune Tube."

❑ Add blue food coloring to water and freeze it in an ice cube tray. When the water is partially frozen, add a craft stick to each cube and then freeze until solid. Give your child a sheet of waxed or butcher paper and invite him or her to use the frozen blue cube to write words that have the long *u* sound spelled *u_e*, *ui*, and *ue*.

❑ Give your child a piece of fruit and say, "Only take a bite each time I say a word with the long *u* sound that you hear in *fruit*." Then say these words slowly: *glue, tub, suit, nut, cute, bow, mule, clown, June, tube, boy, juice, blue,* and *tune*.

❑ Tell your child to listen carefully. Then say, "When I say a word with a long vowel sound, stretch your arms up long over your head. But when I say a word with a short vowel sound, scrunch your body into a ball." Try these words: *soap, cub, hay, pet, cute, cat, pine, leaf, wig,* and *box*. To extend the activity, write the letters *a, e, i, o,* and *u* on separate cards. After your child determines if the vowel sound in the word is long or short, say, "Now hold up the letter that stands for that sound."

Match Word Parts

Draw a line from a word part in the first column to one in the second column. Write the whole word on the line.

gar   tle   _____

tur   cus   _____

can   den   _____

cir   dle   _____

 Say each picture name. How many parts does it have? Follow the color key to color.

1 part=	2 parts=	3 parts=

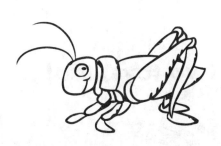  

Reviewing syllabication

355

Review Sound-Alikes

Circle the two words in the sentence that sound alike but have different spellings and meanings. How fast can you say the tongue-twisters?

Ann ate eight apples.

Sid and Sam see the sea.

A bee may be by Bill.

The wind blew
the blue blanket.

Ron rode on a rocky road.

You take two toys, too!

Reviewing homophones

Review ou, ow, oi, oy

Write ou, ow, oi or oy to finish each word. The word tells who lives in each house. Draw a picture of what the house might look like.

ou

m___se

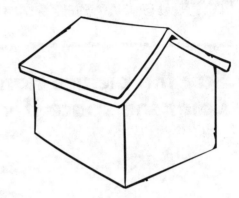

ow

cl___n

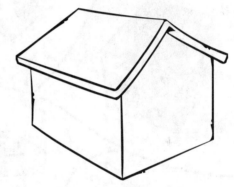

oi

n___sy

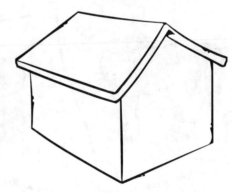

oy

t___

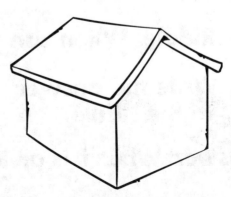

Can You Hear Long u?

The word **cube** has the long u sound.

cube

 Say the picture name.
Color the space if you hear the long **u** sound.

Riddle: When can you catch water in a net?

 Write the answer
to the riddle.   _____

Answer: When it is an ice _____.

*Recognizing pictures that have the long **u** sound; writing long **u** words spelled with silent **e***

Cute Mules

 Follow the directions. Color the huge mule gray. Color the cute mule pink.

 Write 2 words that have the long u sound.

_____   _____

_ _ _ _ _ _ _ _ _ _ _ _ _   _ _ _ _ _ _ _ _ _ _ _ _ _

_____   _____

Writing words with one spelling of the long u sound: u with silent e

Sound of ui and ue

The **ui** in **fru̲i̲t** and the **ue** in **bl̲u̲e̲** have the same sound.

Write the letters **ui** or **ue** to finish each word. Draw a picture to tell what the words say.

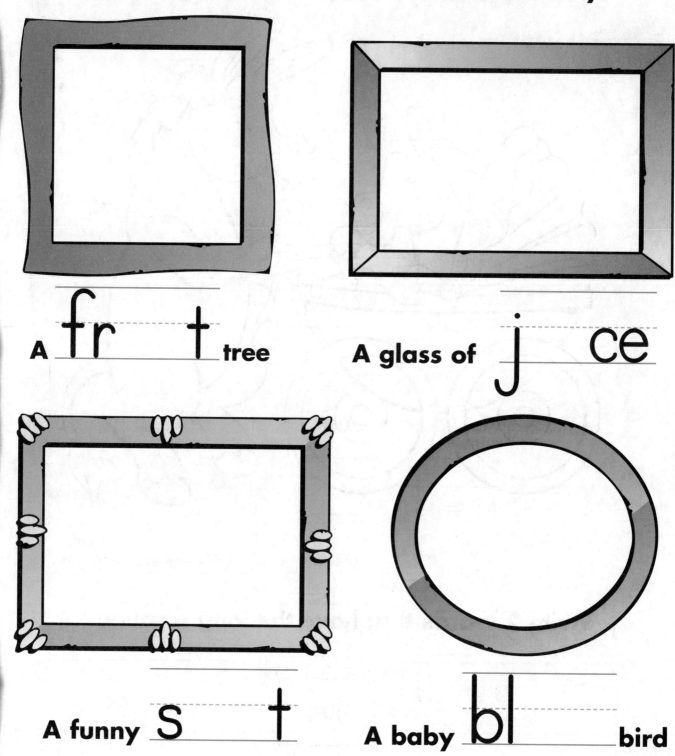

A fr___t tree

A glass of j___ce

A funny s___t

A baby bl___ bird

*Recognizing and writing words with the vowel combinations **ui** and **ue***

Glue's Clues

Help Sue find the glue. Color each block that has the same vowel sound as in glue. Write each word you color on one of the lines.

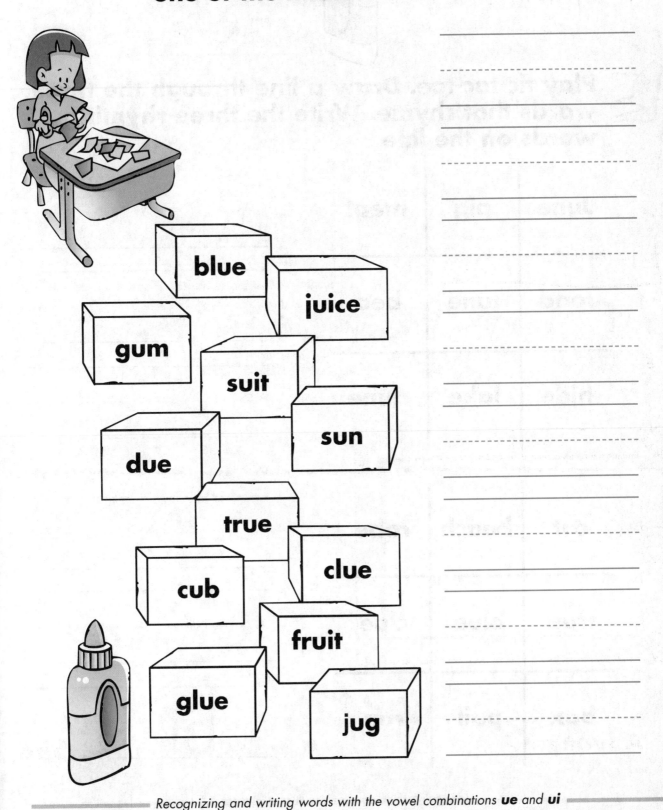

blue

juice

gum

suit

sun

due

true

cub

clue

fruit

glue

jug

_____

_____

_____

_____

_____

_____

_____

_____

_____

_____

*Recognizing and writing words with the vowel combinations **ue** and **ui***

Rhyme Time

 and  have the same ending sounds.

and rhyme.

 Play tic-tac-toe. Draw a line through the three words that rhyme. Write the three rhyming words on the line.

June	pig	meat
toad	tune	bed
hide	lake	dune

_____

_____

_____

_____

_____

cat	beach	robe
true	blue	clue
box	pail	run

_____

_____

_____

_____

_____

*Identifying rhyming words with **u_e** and **ue***

More Rhyme Time Fun

 Say each picture name. Circle the word in each row that rhymes with the picture name.

   house   make   rule   mud

   bun   tune   jet   jeep

   suit   frame   boat   frog

   top   crib   toast   cube

   black   bake   glue   bed

*Identifying rhyming words with **u_e, ui,** and **ue***

More Rhyme Time Fun

 Write your own rhyme. Use the words in the box to finish each line.

tune   June   dune

_____

In the jolly month of _____ ,

We sing a happy _____ ,

As we bounce, bounce, bounce,

_____

Over a big sand _____ .

glue   true   blue

_____

The color _____ ,

Some sticky _____ ,

Make a pretty picture,

_____

It's _____ !

*Completing rhymes using words with **u_e** and **ue***

Puzzle It Out: Long u

 Look at each picture. Unscramble the letters to write the picture name. Write one letter in each box. Use the words in the word box to help you.

| flute | tune | rude | blue | juice |

d e r u ☐☐☐☐

u t l f e ☐☐☐☐☐

j c u i e ☐☐☐☐☐

u t n e ☐☐☐☐

l b u e ☐☐☐☐

 Look at the letters in the shaded boxes above. Unscramble the letters to write the answer to the question.

What part of a tree can you eat? ☐☐☐☐☐

A "Filler Up!" Picture Hunt

Put an X on 6 things in this picture that have the long u sound. Then say each picture name.

Grease

*Finding objects with the sound of long **u** that are hidden in a picture*

Play concentration!

blue	**blue**
mule	**mule**
flute	**flute**
fruit	**fruit**

Parents: Play concentration with two players. First cut apart the cards and place face down. The first player turns over two cards and reads each word aloud. If they match, the player wins the pair. If not, the cards are turned face down and it's the second player's turn. The player with the most word pairs wins.

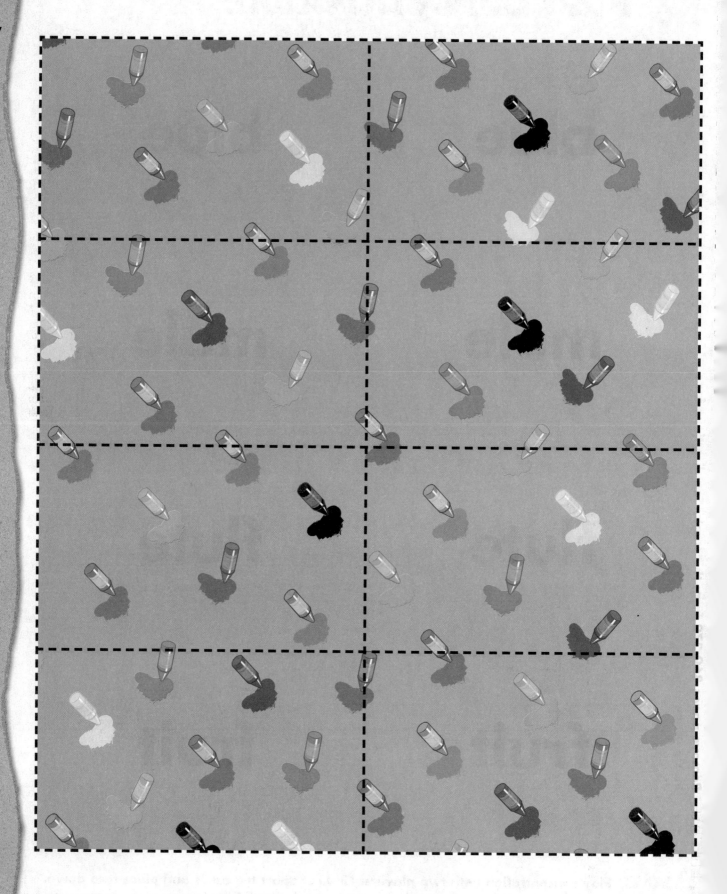

Matching words with long **u**

Parents: Remove pages 369-372 from this book. See directions for making mini storybooks on the inside of the front cover.

SUE
THE MULE

Ruth has a mule.
The mule is named Sue.

Ruth and Sue the Mule went home!

One day, Sue
just sat!

Ruth played a tune
on her flute.
It worked!

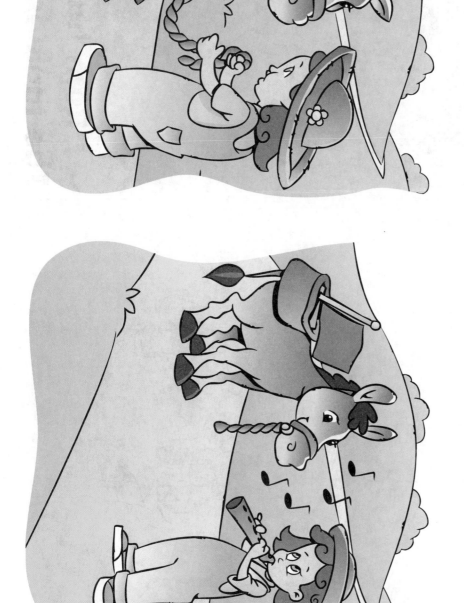

"Get up, Sue!"
cried Ruth.
Sue the Mule did
not move.

Ruth waved a big,
blue flag.
Sue the Mule did
not move.

Ruth pushed and pulled.
Sue the Mule did
not move.

Ruth held out some fruit.
Sue the Mule did
not move.

Sounds of oo

The letters **oo** can stand for different sounds—for the sound in **tooth** or the sound in **book** .

 Do you hear the sound of **oo** in each picture name? Draw a line from each picture to its name.

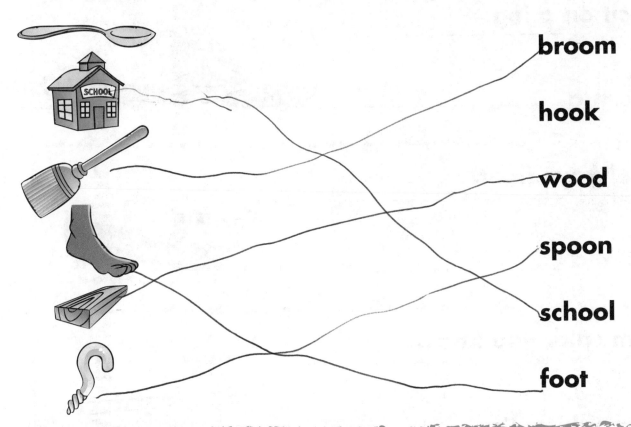

broom

hook

wood

spoon

school

foot

  Write **oo** to finish each word. Say the word. If **oo** has the same sound as in **tooth** color it.

r o o f

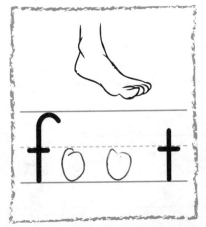

f o o t

g oo se

Recognizing the sounds oo as in tooth and book

Long and Short o Riddles

Write a word from the box to finish each riddle.

nose snow goats frog boat

I sit on a log.
_____

I am a _____ .

I always float.
_____

I am a _____ .

I'm cold, you know.
_____

I'm white. I'm _____ .

I smell a rose.
_____

I am a _____ .

We eat our oats.
_____

We are two _____ .

Reviewing the short and long sounds of **o**

Critter Riddles

What do you call a big kitty?

A FAT CAT

How much does a fly weigh?

NOT A LOT

What do you call a dog in the rain?

A WET PET

What do you call something that a fish hopes for?

A FISH WISH

What do you call a
fast hen?

A QUICK CHICK

What does an insect lay
on her floor?

A BUG RUG

What do you call a
silly rabbit?

A FUNNY BUNNY

What do you call
trousers that an ant
wears?

AN ANT'S PANTS

Practice Test

Say the picture name. Fill in the circle next to the correct word.

- ○ son
- ● sun
- ○ sand

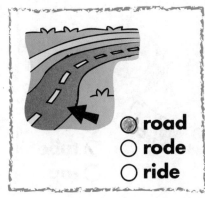
- ● road
- ○ rode
- ○ ride

- ● plain
- ○ plant
- ○ plane

- ● sail
- ○ sale
- ○ sole

- ● cent
- ○ sent
- ○ send

- ○ meet
- ● meat
- ○ make

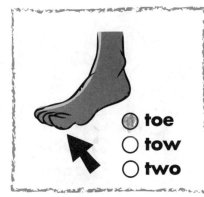
- ● toe
- ○ tow
- ○ two

- ○ made
- ● mail
- ○ male

- ● red
- ○ read
- ○ rest

- ○ to
- ○ too
- ● two

- ○ seat
- ○ see
- ● sea

- ○ tell
- ● tail
- ○ tale

Recognizing homophones

379

Practice Test

Say the picture name. Fill in the circle next to the correct word.

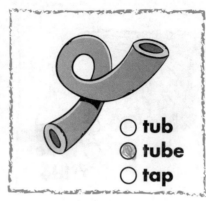
- ○ cent
- ● sub
- ○ sand

- ○ tub
- ● tube
- ○ tap

- ○ flat
- ● flute
- ○ fly

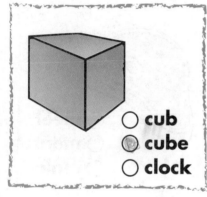
- ○ cub
- ● cube
- ○ clock

- ● tub
- ○ tube
- ○ top

- ● blue
- ○ blob
- ○ bring

- ○ cube
- ● cub
- ○ clock

- ○ made
- ○ must
- ● mug

- ○ deck
- ● duck
- ○ dome

- ○ drip
- ○ drop
- ● drum

- ○ gum
- ● glue
- ○ grab

- ○ sun
- ● suit
- ○ sip

*Recognizing the short and long vowel sounds of **u***

Practice Test

 Say the picture name. Fill in the circle next to the correct word.

- ○ wag
- ○ what
- ● whale

- ○ bee
- ● bread
- ○ breeze

- ○ smell
- ● smile
- ○ smoke

- ○ mill
- ○ mole
- ● mule

- ○ step
- ○ stop
- ● stove

- ○ hat
- ● hay
- ○ hail

- ● jeep
- ○ jet
- ○ jam

- ○ tea
- ● tie
- ○ try

- ○ flag
- ○ fig
- ● frog

- ○ skate
- ○ swim
- ● swing

- ○ track
- ● truck
- ○ train

- ○ flake
- ○ flat
- ○ flip

Recognizing short and long vowel sounds

Practice Test

 Fill in the circle next to each word in the row that has the vowel sound.

Long a
○ snail ○ tape ○ coat ○ vase

Long e
○ peas ○ pie ○ seal ○ meat

Long i
○ kite ○ pine ○ fly ○ fish

Long o
○ bone ○ rope ○ log ○ boat

Long u
○ tub ○ mule ○ cube ○ fuse

*Recognizing words with the long sounds of **a, e, i, o,** and **u***